P9-CMU-826

PRAISE FOR JOE TYE'S OTHER BOOKS:

Never Fear, Never Quit: A Story of Courage and Perseverance

"A beautiful story of courage, love, hope, and faith."
— Mark Victor Hansen, co-author of
Chicken Soup for the Soul

"*Never Fear, Never Quit* says it all. We all have our down times and need the courage and perseverance to lift ourselves back up again. This book can show you the way."
— Ken Blanchard, co-author,
The One Minute Manager

"A prescription for anyone wishing to conquer fear and lead a more creative life."
— C. Everett Koop, M.D.,
former U.S. Surgeon General

Staying on Top When the World's Upside Down

"A practical, readable, compassionate, and helpful book."
— Harold Kushner, author of
When Bad Things Happen to Good People

"A very useful compilation of information applicable to all levels of career planning. Utilization of these suggestions will be beneficial before, during, and following a career change."
— Zig Ziglar, author of *Over the Top*

OTHER BOOKS BY JOE TYE:

Never Fear, Never Quit: A Story of Courage and Perseverance
Personal Best
Staying on Top When the World's Upside Down
The Shepherd King
The Healing Tree
It's Better to be a Three-Legged Coyote than a Four-Legged Fur Coat
The Self Transformation Workbook

AUDIO AND VIDEO PROGRAMS BY JOE TYE

The Twelve Core Action Values of Never Fear, Never Quit
Courageous Entrepreneurship Home Study Course
The Janitor in Your Attic
Success Warrior (Editor's Choice, Success Magazine)
Radical Faith
The Four Pillars of Success and Happiness
The Ten Commandments of Creativity
It's a Beautiful Evening for Flying (with Doug Peters)

For more information about how you can join the Never Fear, Never Quit movement, or to request a complete catalog, call 800-644-3889.

Your Dreams Are Too Small

Joe Tye

Jim —
Dream Big &
Expect Miracles,
JT

RHODES & EASTON
TRAVERSE CITY, MICHIGAN

Copyright © 2000 by Joe Tye

All rights reserved. No part of this book may be reproduced or transmitted in any form or by any means, electronic or mechanical, including photocopying, recording, or by any information storage and retrieval system, without permission in writing from the publisher.

Published by RHODES & EASTON
121 East Front Street, #401
Traverse City, MI 49684

Publisher's Cataloging-in-Publication Data
Tye, Joe.
        Your dreams are too small / Joe Tye.– Traverse City, Mich. : Rhodes
        & Easton, 1999.
              p.   cm.
        ISBN 0-9649401-8-3

        1. Inspiration.   I. Title.
                    1999
                    dc—21   CIP

PROJECT COORDINATION BY JENKINS GROUP, INC.

02 01 00 ▲ 5 4

Printed in the United States of America

This book is dedicated to Annie Tye,
who could teach us all a thing or two about
mountain-sized dreams. No organization could ask
for a more conscientious worker;
no father could hope for a more wonderful daughter.

CONTENTS

CONTENTS

ACKNOWLEDGMENTS

As *NEVER FEAR, NEVER QUIT* HAS GROWN, MANY PEOPLE HAVE HELPED ME grow, to learn how to dream bigger myself, along with it. I am thankful to all of my students, and especially members of the NFNQ Entrepreneurship Coaching program. Sue Engel has been a key part of what NFNQ is all about, and Dick Schwab has been an invaluable business strategy advisor. The pioneers who became the first official NFNQ organizations have helped to define much bigger dimensions for our mission: special thanks to Leigh Cox, Brian Hoefle, and the entire team at Navapache Regional Medical Center in Show Low, Arizona; Patrick Charmel and the team at Griffin Hospital; Todd Linden and the team at Grinnell Regional Medical Center; and to Thom Greenlaw and the membership of the Environmental Management Association. I've learned from many big-dreaming entrepreneurs, including Tom Hui, Thomas J. Winninger, Raymond Aaron and Herb Wilson. During some particularly challenging times, I especially appreciated the support of Ray Glass and everyone at Hawkeye State Bank, Denny McDonnel, Ed Foreman, Art Berg, Bill Townsley, Rick Nielsen, Doug Peters, Bruce Williams, Lori Prokop, Dave Bruno, and Nick Opalich. Special thanks to Jerry Jenkins, Nathan Tarsa, Margaret Alexander, Kim Hornyak, Eric Norton, Kathy Prentice and the rest of the staff at Jenkins Group, Inc. for their unflagging support in the development of this book. My brothers Steven and Allen have been a huge support. Most of all, I thank God for blessing me with Sally, Annie, and Doug, who are the source of, and the reason for, all my big dreams.

INTRODUCTION

THE TIMES IN WHICH WE LIVE, AT THE BREAK POINT BETWEEN TWO millennia, has been called "the age of anxiety" by some commentators, and with good reason. The job as we know it — the rock of stability on which so many of us have depended for economic and career security, and even for a sense of personal identity — is going away. So too is the traditional notion of a career path. Those accelerating and irrevocable changes in our economy have caused substantial insecurity for many people.

Yet, this is also an era of unparalleled abundance and opportunity. If in the past decade U.S. corporations have eliminated millions of jobs, even more millions have been created by smaller businesses created by entrepreneurs, many of whom are refugees from the corporate world. And by the thousands, these new entrepreneurs are creating unprecedented wealth and prosperity for themselves and others. More important, they are following their own dreams, not those imposed upon them by some faceless corporation.

On a day-to-day basis, the most important choice any of us make is the choice of what to see in the world around us, and how to respond to what we perceive. Do you choose to see the anxiety or to see the opportunity? To be an optimist or a pessimist? To interpret the knot in your stomach as a symptom of terror or of exhilaration?

Do you choose to stay in the little foxhole you've dug for yourself, or to have the courage to leave the familiar world of your comfort zone in the pursuit of a bigger dream? To cling desperately to what you have now, or to stretch out your arms toward something more magnificent, even if it may mean letting go and taking risk?

Above all, are you willing to change what you see when you look in the mirror? To discard the old self-limiting self-image and replace it with a more positive and self-empowering one? To deliberately and consciously raise your self-esteem so that you convince yourself of this truth: that you are both capable of achieving those big dreams, and deserving of the fruits of your success.

Chances are the only thing standing between you and the achievement of your most precious dreams is you. If you can follow the path set out by Charlie McKeever in this book, if you can overcome the artificial limitations you've imposed upon yourself, and if you can learn to dream big dreams and believe in your own destiny to fulfill those dreams, then this will become your age of abundance and opportunity.

Dream a big dream, make it a memory of the future, and expect a miracle!

Never Fear, Never Quit!

Joe Tye
March, 2000
Solon, Iowa

1

✎

SEE THE WORLD AS IT REALLY IS — NOT AS IT USED TO BE, AS YOU WISH IT WERE, OR AS YOU FEAR IT MIGHT BE

CHARLIE MCKEEVER HAD SENSED THAT THINGS WERE GOING DOWNHILL. First he noticed a faint wisp of apprehension hanging over his head on the way to work. At the time it seemed a benign little cloud that would blow over. But in the succeeding days it grew bigger until this morning he woke up with a dark thunderhead of dread blocking his enthusiasm and optimism. "Today the storm will come," the cloud seemed to promise.

Charlie had started with Logistics Plus as a junior analyst right out of college, forsaking the MBA route taken by most of the other kids he'd become friends with through St. Johns' Entrepreneurship Club. "LPI is the hottest consulting company in the country today," the recruiter boasted. "We're growing fast, and the demand for the type of management consulting we do will keep on growing as technology gets more comprehensive." Charlie had liked the recruiter immediately — bright and enthusiastic, and barely out of school himself.

"The opportunities for advancement are limited only by your energy and initiative. Who knows, you could become the youngest partner in the history of this firm — you've certainly got the intelligence and the work ethic. It's really the perfect job: the excitement of entrepreneurship plus the security of working for an established firm."

Charlie had worked hard for the past fourteen years and had been well rewarded. He and his wife Pam bought a nice house in the suburbs and their children attended an exclusive private school. But he never did make partner. Each year there was a different reason — no vacancies, the firm was having a tough year, and finally that he lacked an MBA degree. But the disappointment was always eased with a healthy pay raise and the promise that he would be at the top of the list for consideration the next time around.

Until this year. When his performance appraisal was completed three months ago, Charlie was, as usual, praised for his hard work and dedication. "But we really need you to raise the bar," Dick Dierdron, the new managing partner, told him. "When I took this office last year, I made it pretty clear that I expected everyone to produce new business. You just haven't stepped up to the plate. You haven't brought any new clients into the firm, nor have you extended the contracts of current clients."

"It's no secret the competition is heating up, and that we've lost some important business to the Lipton Group." Dierdron scowled as he spit out the name of LPI's toughest competitor. "Profits are not what they should be. The partners," and he said this as though speaking of some outside body over which he had no influence, "have told me that we'll have to make cutbacks if the situation is not remedied, and remedied very quickly."

Dierdron leaned back in his high-backed leather chair. "You're one of our best consultants, Charlie. We can't afford to lose you. You're the best teacher we have for new kids coming into the firm." Dierdron adjusted his gold cufflinks, signifying the meeting was almost over. "But you've got to bring in business, Charlie. Don't just sit here in the office waiting for someone to bring it to you."

Dierdron was about to stand up when Charlie blurted out, "When am I supposed to be finding all this new business, Dick? I'm working about eighty hours a week now, and you've just charged me with installing the new computer system." In fourteen years Charlie had never even raised his voice — especially not at a partner. But suddenly it seemed like a mental dam was stretching to the breaking point, about to release a flood of emotions. "I'm in here before the night shift guard leaves every morning and I'm still here when the janitor locks up every night, including Saturday. I've given my life — for cryin' out loud Dick, I hardly know my own kids! Other parents talk about coaching their kids' soccer teams. I don't even have time to see my kids' soccer team play!"

Now Charlie was leaning across the desk. "Just when do you want me making cold calls, Dick? Between the hours of midnight and six a.m. when I'm not working on projects? Or do you want me to stop running up billable hours?"

Charlie took a deep breath. "I'm sorry, Dick, but I just can't do it all. I don't know what you expect of me. I'm working as hard as I can, and even now I can't keep up. But if you want new business, you know me, I'll do the best I can to bring in new business."

Dierdron scribbled something onto a sheet of paper and passed it across the desk. "That's your raise for this year, Charlie. With everything so tight, we're not doing very much for anyone." Charlie picked up the paper and stuffed it into his shirt pocket without looking at it, and stood to go. Dierdron rose as well. "Charlie," he said, "I want you to be clear about one thing."

Charlie stopped by the door. "What's that, Dick?"

"You're working these crazy hours because you choose to."

Dierdron let the accusation hang in the air until Charlie retorted, "What do you mean, because I choose to? The work must be done."

"Of course the work must be done. But that doesn't mean you have to do it all by yourself. After fourteen years, you're still doing a lot of the same kind of thing you did as a brand-new junior analyst. You haven't grown into the work we expect of an experienced associate — like growing new business. You've got to learn how to delegate more, to ask for help more, so that I can delegate more important work to you."

This was the first time in his tenure with LPI that Charlie had been directly criticized, and he could feel the hair rising on the back of his neck.

Dierdron cut off Charlie's train of thought. "It's Thursday afternoon. Why don't you get one of the new analysts to pick up for you. Take a long weekend away from the office to think. Are you going to grow with us or not? You're at a fork in the road, Charlie. It's time to make a decision, time to commit."

Dierdron walked back to his desk, picked up the phone and punched in a number. "Hey Ben, it's Dick. I need to talk to you about that Consolidated Banking deal. Is this a good time?"

Charlie went home early, but was back in the office on Friday, careful to avoid Dick Dierdron. He only worked half a day on Saturday, and surprised his son by showing up at his soccer game that afternoon.

Things fell back into a routine over the next few months. Charlie brought several junior analysts in on the big computer project, made a few cold calls and even bagged a three-month extension on a consulting contract.

He'd almost forgotten the performance appraisal as he burrowed back into his work. But still that gathering cloud of dread hung overhead. A premonition of pain to come.

It came at 3:30 Friday afternoon. Dierdron was not one to make small talk. "The partners have decided that we must make reductions, Charlie, and your position has been eliminated, effective now. As you know, your contract included a generous severance provision. When you leave my office, Marcella will give you your final paycheck. The partners have asked me to convey to you their deepest appreciation for your dedicated service. And on a personal note, I want you to know that if there's anything I can do to be of assistance, you only need to call."

Dierdron came out from behind his desk and extended his right hand. "Charlie, now that you are no longer an employee here, I can tell you something I've believed for a long time, but simply could not say." When Charlie refused to take Dierdron's hand, his former boss stepped closer and put a hand on Charlie's shoulder, looking him square in the eye.

"Wake up, Charlie. You don't belong hidden away in a cubicle with your nose buried in computer printouts. You're too smart, too talented. Why don't you use that talent to build something?" Charlie looked at the floor.

"You're not an analyst, Charlie, you're not a consultant. People like you can make big things happen. People like you change the world. You've got more potential than all the partners here wrapped together. What are you waiting for?"

Charlie broke away. He looked at the photo of Mt. Everest that was on the wall opposite Dierdron's desk. The inscription: Big Hills Are The Only Ones Worth Climbing.

Charlie hesitated for a moment.

"I'm really sorry, Charlie. I meant it when I said I'll help in any way if you just..."

Charlie stepped out of the office and pulled the door shut behind him, cutting off the tail end of Dierdron's sentence.

Charlie sat on the bayside deck of The Patio, a favorite after-work hangout of the professional crowd. The sun was high and a soft breeze was blowing across the bay. This was the first time he'd ventured forth from his house since being fired two weeks earlier, and the first time in many years that he'd sat in the sun on a weekday with nothing more important to do.

But Cheryl von Noyes would be arriving at any moment. An old friend from the Entrepreneurship Club at St. Johns, she had recently lost her job as controller of a local manufacturing company. Charlie knew she'd received only a meager severance and suspected she'd be pretty desperate, so he didn't want to make her feel bad by being too upbeat himself. He slumped down in his chair and looked out over the water, conjuring images of Dick Dierdron giving him the axe.

"Hey, Charlie McKeever!" Cheryl had slipped up to the table while Charlie was trying to resurrect his anger. "You don't look very happy for a man who's just been liberated after fourteen years of hard labor!" Cheryl plopped into the chair beside Charlie and leaned over to wrap him in a bear hug.

"Cheryl," Charlie exclaimed, trying to keep his balance as his chair tipped toward his friend, "you sure are happy for someone who's just been canned!"

"Are you kidding," Cheryl laughed, "I wasn't canned, I was let out of the can! And with every new day of freedom, I appreciate all the more how big a favor they did for me."

"So how are you doing, Charlie?"

He sighed and looked at his feet, now sporting sandals instead of the polished wingtips he'd worn nearly every day for the past fourteen years. "Oh, well, I guess..." Charlie sighed again "I guess I'm doing as well as any unemployed bum could be doing, after his life's work and his dreams have been ripped from him." The phrase sounded every bit as eloquent as he'd hoped it would when he'd rehearsed it earlier that day. "I'm looking around, but it's pretty hard when you've got the Scarlet "F" — Fired! — as the last line on your resume."

"Oh, Charlie! You always did know how to crack me up!" Charlie was soon smiling himself, overlooking his annoyance that she was laughing at him, at his carefully prepared little speech. "What's so funny?"

"Sorry, but as you were talking I had this picture pop into my mind of you and your family sitting under a bridge, warming your hands over a trashcan fire. Can you imagine anything more ridiculous, especially for the guy voted most likely to win big by the Entrepreneurship Club?"

"Well, yeah, as a matter of fact I can," Charlie sniffed. She hardly looked any older, he thought. Her hair was cut short in the style that so many women executives seemed to be wearing. Her white shirt and red blazer prompted Charlie to wonder if she had a job interview scheduled later that afternoon. On her lapel was a gold pin forming "FPN" in bold block letters. There was a small jewel at one end, with indentations evidently marking the places of future gems. "You must have a new job already lined up to be taking this so lightly."

"Well," she smiled, "yes and no. But I take it from your sad face that you're still looking. How's it going?"

This was not at all what Charlie had envisioned for this meeting. Not only was Cheryl not a broken woman, she was positively ebullient. Instead of raising her up from the depths, he now saw the likelihood that he was going to bring her down. He wanted to say something, but was afraid he might cry if he tried. Cheryl's face grew suddenly serious. "I'll tell you, Charlie, I'm not looking for a job. I am determined that never again will I place my future in the hands of someone whose only interest is how much money my work puts into their pocket. "You know what the letters J-O-B stand for? 'Jilted, Obsolete, and Broke!'

"But Cheryl," Charlie protested, "not everyone's cut out for entrepreneurship. It can be a big risk."

"I'm not talking about entrepreneurship, Charlie," she replied. "I'm talking about getting back to what's really important. To having work that makes a difference, work that has meaning beyond just making a paycheck. Work that you can be passionate about, work that you love to do and can do with love. Wait, listen to this..." Cheryl pulled a small book from her purse. "Let me read a poem to you that changed my attitude about work." Charlie read the book's cover, *Little Nuggets of Wisdom* by McZen. Cheryl read aloud:

> *Someone with a job*
> *is never secure;*
> *Someone with a calling*
> *is never unemployed.*

"It's true, Charlie. If you only have a job, you'll never be secure, no matter how much money you make. If your work is a calling, you'll always have something important to do."

Charlie snorted, "The only calling I want to hear right now is a headhunter telling me about a high-paying job."

"So you can wind up jilted, obsolete, and broke again?" Cheryl actually looked angry. "Life's too short to trade it away for money, and if you don't love your work like it's a calling, all the money in the world won't bring you peace."

"I don't know," Charlie replied. "I wouldn't even mind losing a job if I got one of those golden parachute packages. I could get used to being insecure if I had a bank vault loaded to the brim."

"Don't bank on it," Cheryl retorted. "You remember reading about Mad Dog Dunleavy, the so-called turnaround artist who would come into a company and hack away thousands of jobs to pump up short-term profits — and the stock price — then walk away with a multi-million dollar bonus before the empty shell collapsed behind him?"

"Yeah, sure," Charlie replied. "Only he didn't get away fast enough at the Top Drawer Company — the shell collapsed on top of him and he got fired."

"My point exactly," crowed Cheryl. "No matter how high up, someone with a job is never secure."

"No," Charlie shot back "my point exactly. "Mad Dog was a failure, but you know as well as I do that his lawyers will squeeze millions out of Top Drawer to make him go away. I could live for a long time with that kind of insecurity!"

Cheryl leaned back in her chair and looked at Charlie, and Charlie sensed that she might not like what she was seeing. "Mad Dog is exactly what is wrong with our country today. The man has no values, no guiding vision, and no central principles beyond padding his bank account. All he cares about is fattening up a bank account that he built on the backs of the people whose livelihoods he shattered in the name of boosting quarterly profits."

"Why, Cheryl," Charlie said, "if I didn't know any better I'd think you're becoming a socialist."

"Quite the contrary, Charlie. In fact, I think what Mad Dog and people like him are doing is the opposite of capitalism, and of entrepreneurship. Capitalists and entrepreneurs create value, mad dogs destroy it. Someone like Mad Dog Dunleavy doesn't belong in the same breath with Bill Hewlett and Dave Packard, with Herb Kelleher or Mary Kay Ash and the others we studied in school. You wanna know what the difference is, Charlie? Those people, those heroes of American capitalism, had a dream, a dream that involved creating jobs and growing people, not destroying jobs and humiliating people."

Cheryl sat back in her chair. "Charlie, I just can't see you, of all people, wanting to be anything like Mad Dog Dunleavy. In school, we all wanted to be like you — Charlie, the man of mountain-sized dreams."

"It's not easy, Cheryl, when the kids come along, and the mortgage payments and the car payments, and pretty soon college tuition. I guess if I had a bank account the size of Mad Dog's, I'd be a little more adventurous."

"You think Mad Dog's happy?" Before Charlie had time to answer, Cheryl went on. "Let me tell you, the other day I was going in for an appointment with my shrink and..." Cheryl noticed Charlie's shock at the confession and interjected, "Yeah, I have problems that I can't figure out on my own, and I've learned that being ashamed to ask for help when you need it is a sign of weakness, not strength." Then she continued, "So guess who was in the waiting room when I came out? Go on Charlie, give it a shot — who was sitting there, looking miserable as a starving hound in a rainstorm? That's right Charlie, the Mad Dog himself."

Charlie looked to Cheryl like a poor beaten dog himself. "Sorry I got so carried away, Charlie. I just hate to see you wasting your life, chasing this phantom of security. You can't get it from a job, you can't get it from money. It's got to be from something bigger. You have to have a mission, a vision, a calling."

"What does he do for you?" asked Charlie, still not looking up.

"What does who do?"

"Your, uhm, your shrink?"

"Dr. Connors? He helps me see things the way they really are. Not as they used to be. Not as I wish they were or think they ought to be, not as I'm afraid they might become. Just simply as they are."

Charlie looked at her, not quite comprehending.

"You just lost a job that, truth be told, you really didn't like and certainly wouldn't have been doing except for the money. Was that a good thing or a bad thing?"

Charlie shrugged.

"The answer is yes, Charlie. Good or bad, it depends on how you choose to see it. That's what Dr. Connors helps me figure out. Part of becoming a real adult is to see the world as it is, without having that perception distorted by your ego, your emotions, and your ambition. And to accept it as it is, without judging good or bad, because that's the first step to being able to change it."

"Is he nice? This Dr. Connors, is he... I mean... What I am really trying to ask, Cheryl, is if you have his phone number in case I want to call him."

Cheryl smiled, warmed by a flood of affection for the wounded man of mountain-sized dreams. Though he probably never even knew it, it was his vulnerability, his willingness to ask for help, that made him the natural leader of the Entrepreneurship Club. She lifted her purse, extracted one of her business cards, and wrote Dr. Connor's name and number across the top.

"FPN," Charlie commented, already nervous at the prospect of making an appointment with a psychiatrist, "I noticed that on your pin, too. What does it stand for?"

"Future Perfect Now," Cheryl replied. "It's my new business."

"Future... Perfect ... Now?" Charlie asked. "What is it? What do you do?"

Cheryl pulled another book from her purse. "This, Charlie, is my *Dreamcyclopedia*. It contains photographs, news clippings, and other records of my future." Charlie smiled as he asked, "Your future? Have you discussed this, ahh, dream book with your shrink?"

"Yes Charlie, actually we're working on it together. Rather than trying to take me back through everything that was wrong in my past, he wants me to think about everything that's right about my future."

Charlie looked at Cheryl, then at her *Dreamcyclopedia*, searching for some hint of a punch line. When it didn't come, he asked, "Well, it sounds, umm, interesting. Will you tell me more about it?"

"Not now Charlie. You're not ready." Cheryl put the book back in her purse and stood up to leave. "Frankly, Charlie, your dreams are too small. As long as your primary fixation is on money and security, FPN has nothing to offer you. Dr. Connors works with a lot of displaced executives. See if he can help you figure things out. Then maybe we can talk again."

She gave Charlie a quick hug and was gone.

Midway through the third appointment, Dr. Connors walked over to the picture window and looked down. It had never occurred to Charlie to wonder what was on the other side of that window, engrossed as he had been in telling Dr. Connors his story. He was beginning to wonder what Cheryl saw in the doctor, since so far Charlie had done almost all the talking.

"Come on over," Dr. Connors said. "Take a look at this."

Charlie looked down at a swimming pool shimmering in the court-yard sun. "It's a therapy pool for PT patients," the doctor explained. "Think of that pool as your subconscious mind, Charlie. It's the real you, the authentic you, the you that has total clarity, perfect serenity, and that is connected with infinite wisdom and knowledge of all things."

Charlie looked into the pool, trying to imagine himself peaceful and all knowing. The surface was so calm he could read the lane marker numbers on the bottom as clearly as if there had been no water in the pool.

"Uh-oh," said Dr. Connors, "here comes the little troublemaker who has deceived you into thinking that he's the real you." He point-ed down to the walkway where a therapist was trying to restrain a young boy with a noticeable limp who was surging toward the pool.

"What do you mean, the little trouble-..."

"Shh!" Dr. Connors held up a finger. "Watch what happens to the letters at the bottom of the pool." The little boy leaped into the pool, his splash forcing the therapist to make a quick retreat. The young diver came up laughing.

"Read the words embedded in the tile at the deep end of the pool." Dr. Connors instructed.

"You're kidding, right?" The surface of the pool was now so rippled that Charlie couldn't even see the bottom, much less make out any words that might be printed there.

"Sit down, Charlie." Dr. Connors perched atop his desk as Charlie took his place back on the sofa. "Now, close your eyes and relax. Let the image of the pool, before it was disrupted by that little boy, come back into your mind. And to help you hold away the disrupting influ-ence of the little troublemaker for a moment, I'm going to recite some words that are probably very familiar to you. 'The Lord is my shepherd, I shall not...'"

"Goodness and mercy!" Charlie blurted out. "Those are the words in the pool! I saw it in my mind as clear as day, as soon as I knew you were reciting the Twenty-third Psalm!"

Dr. Connors laughed. "The good sisters have left their mark everywhere at the hospital; even at the bottom of the therapy pool!" Dr. Connors returned to his desk, then spoke again. "When I was in med school, someone had posted a sign on our locker room bulletin board that asked 'What is it you know but are pretending to not know?' Tell me, Charlie, what did you know fourteen years ago when you were involved in the Entrepreneurship Club that you are pretending to not know today?"

Charlie closed his eyes again, let his thinking drift back to the classroom where they had met every Thursday evening to share their dreams. As clearly as he'd seen the letters on the bottom of the pool, Charlie now saw the faces of his fellow students as he described his dream of building a worldwide organization of people who were not only committed to making the world a better place, but who received economic rewards commensurate with their individual contribution toward that goal. "My God," Charlie thought, "look at them. They actually took me seriously! They thought I was really going to make it happen."

From a deep recess of his mind, Charlie heard his mother's voice yelling out: "Not yet Charlie! Don't you go in until I can come and watch you." Then his own voice as a little boy shrieking, "The pool! Last one in's a rotten egg!" Charlie looked at the faces around him in the classroom. Cheryl was speaking: "and Charlie is so right! The most important thing about what he's saying is..."

SPLASH!!

The image of the classroom erupted into ripples. "You can't keep me out of the pool," the little boy's voice was shouting as he splashed, creating chaos and confusion. The earlier clarity of his thoughts dissipated into a kaleidoscope of images, complete with a soundtrack of criticism, disappointment and pity — all directed at him.

"What did you see, Charlie?"

Charlie opened his eyes and realized he was crying. "I don't know. Cheryl was trying to tell me ... it was something really important ... but he —the trouble maker—jumped in the pool before she said it."

"Charlie, we're almost at the end of our hour, but I'd like to do something I almost never do. Because it's coming up on noon, my next hour is open. I'd like to help you learn more about that little troublemaker who's playing around in your pool. Can you stay?"

Charlie forced a smile. "I'm unemployed, Doc. I've got no place to go and all the time in the world to get there."

Dr. Connors pulled the blinds to darken the room. He asked Charlie to close his eyes, relax, and let his mind just drift freely.

When Charlie seemed sufficiently relaxed, Dr. Connors continued. "Now, I am going to describe several situations to you, and you tell me in a sentence or two what you think is going on. Don't worry about trying to get what you think is the right answer, just describe the first scenario that pops into your mind. OK?"

Charlie nodded and the doctor went on. "Number one. You've been called into your boss's office. He's there with the company lawyer, the head of security, a uniformed police officer, and another man you don't recognize. They're all frowning and everyone seems distinctly uncomfortable the moment you step into the room. What's about to happen — first thing that comes to your mind?"

"I'm about to be fired and escorted to my car by the security guard and the cop to make sure I don't cause trouble or steal anything on the way out."

"Alright," said Dr. Connors, "here's the next one. You've applied for a job, one that you really want. They call to say you are their preferred candidate, but they want to check a few references, including the boss who just fired you. One week later you get a letter regretfully informing you that you were not selected for the job. What happened?"

"That's obvious. The jerk wasn't content with just trashing my job, he had to trash my career as well, so he gave one of those politically correct references that between the lines says that he thinks I'm a loser and they could do better."

Dr. Connors paused for a moment and Charlie could hear the scratching of his pen. "Here's number three. It takes you ten months to find another job, but the chemistry just isn't there with the new boss, and very quickly you get fired. The next search takes almost a year, and in your third month on the job the company announces a layoff that wipes out your position. Another two years go by and you still don't have a job in the traditional sense. Describe your circumstances."

Charlie groaned. "Pam and I have moved back in with my parents and I contribute to the household budget by mowing lawns and delivering pizza."

"OK. Next one. Instead of taking a traditional job, you decide to start your own business." Connors noted that Charlie grimaced. "Things come together much more slowly than you had anticipated, and you exhaust every available source of cash — savings, retirement accounts, everything. You're starting to bounce checks and still have no sales on the books. What happens next?"

"Bankruptcy." Charlie spit the word out. When Dr. Connors remained silent, he added, "Bankruptcy, humiliation, divorce. I'm sure you've seen it all, doc, what comes next? Drugs and alcohol? Suicide?"

"Relax, Charlie. Let me ask the questions for now. Now, for these next three, I want you to put yourself in the state of mind you were in right after you got fired. Try to bring back all the emotions you were feeling, as though it had just happened."

Charlie looked as if he'd been kicked in the stomach. Connors went on. "You're sitting at home going through the want ads when suddenly a memory pops into your head from college days. What is that memory, the first thing you think of?"

"Failing calculus my freshman year."

"Number two. You're sitting at home going through the want ads and the phone rings. It's a headhunter who tells you that you're one of two final candidates for the job you really want. She says that you know the other candidate, but she can't reveal who it is. Who do you immediately suspect?"

"Jeremy Potts. Lord, I don't have a chance. Even I would offer the job to Potts before I gave it to me."

"One more, Charlie. You get a call from your banker. He tells you that the big conglomerate to which they sold your mortgage has a policy against carrying loans on people who are unemployed. If you don't have a job within six weeks, they're going to demand full and immediate payment of your home loan. You take out a pad of paper and start making a list of all your options. Tell me what's on your list."

Charlie thought for a minute. "All I need is to have a job? Any job? Well, I could get something down at the Stay-Put plant. They're always looking for people for the night shift, and really don't care what your qualifications are as long as you can make your arms move in time with the assembly line. I could ... let's see. I could go to Pam's dad and ask him to list me as one of his employees, but with the understanding that he didn't have to pay me a salary. I could always go back to delivering pizza like I did in college. Is that enough?"

"That's enough Charlie. Go ahead and open your eyes and let's talk about what you've said. What you just completed is a standardized test. The first series of questions measure where you fall on the optimism-pessimism scale, and the second set measures how you respond to anxiety. Taken together, Charlie, these two tests often show how seriously your conscious mind — if you will, the little troublemaker in the pool — can distort your perception of reality. Actually, there is a correct response to each of the questions you just answered. And you missed every single one, Charlie, which suggests to me that your future success and happiness depend on doing some reprogramming up here," and Dr. Connors pointed to his own temple.

"Let's go through them one by one," Connors said. "In the first scenario, when you were called into your boss's office, you automatically assumed you were about to be fired. In fact, the boss's car had been stolen from the parking lot. The person you didn't know was his insurance agent. The only reason you were called was to see if you'd noticed anything unusual, and for the boss to ask you for a ride home."

"Oh come on!" Charlie protested. "That's so unlikely! You can't just..."

"Charlie," Dr. Connors cut him off, "this question measures your tendency to jump to pessimistic conclusions. At least you didn't automatically assume that you were about to be arrested because someone had planted illegal drugs in your desk — hey, you'd be surprised how many people do — but your response is toward the negative end of the scale. It's especially important for you to watch out for this, because over time people tend to find what they're looking for."

"Are you saying that after fourteen years I got fired because I expected to be fired?"

"You tell me, Charlie. Did you expect to be fired? Were there times you imagined it happening? Planned what you would say when it did? In fact, Charlie, were there times that in your imagination getting fired was actually a relief, the lifting of a burden? Were there times when being able to tell the boss what you really thought felt pretty good?"

"Guilty on all counts." Charlie smiled sheepishly.

"The second scenario, where your boss was asked for a reference. Here's what actually happened. The company hit hard times and imposed an across-the-board hiring freeze. But rather than tell you that, it was easier to send the standard rejection letter. Your boss actually gave you a very nice recommendation."

Charlie looked skeptical.

"Remember what you told me his last words were as you were walking out? Something about wanting to help? Do you think he was lying to you? Laying a trap so he could deliberately wreck your opportunity to make a living?"

"Well, when you put it that way."

"It's another of the problematic behaviors of the little trouble-maker in the pool. Needing to have someone to blame when things go wrong, rather than accepting that sometimes things simply go wrong. He ends up creating villains where there are none. But if you react as though there are villains out there, you invariably create enemies — in your own mind first, and then in the real world as you respond to situations in inappropriate ways."

Charlie shifted uncomfortably, recalling the satisfaction he'd felt at closing the door on Dierdron's parting offer to help. It was sincerely meant, Charlie knew in his heart. Dierdron would have given such a glowing reference it would have embarrassed him to hear it. And if that's true, Charlie thought, then maybe he was also telling the truth when he said I had more potential than to spend the rest of my career at LPI. Instead of being a villain, maybe he actually believed he was doing me a favor by pushing me out the door.

"In the third scenario, where you lost two jobs almost as soon as you got them, your response was that you moved back in with your parents, and took on menial jobs. What really happened," and at this Dr. Connors smiled at the paradox of claiming to know more about Charlie's future than he did himself, "is that you went back to Logistics Precision and signed them up as the first customer in what very quickly became a multi-million dollar business called McKeever Enterprises."

Charlie rolled his eyes.

"Wake up, Charlie," Dr. Connors admonished. "Isn't that a more likely scenario than moving back home and delivering pizza?"

Charlie nodded, reluctantly.

"You were mentally projecting the inevitability of the worst possible outcome. I see it all the time. Someone loses a job, and next thing you know in their own mind their family is starving because they're the only one who can't seem to find another job, even in this booming economy."

Charlie smiled, even more sheepishly this time. He'd been doing an awful lot of awfulizing lately.

"In scenario number four, where you ran out of money and started bouncing checks, your first response was a declaration of bankruptcy. Actually, Charlie, that's the all-too-common practice of blowing things out of proportion, something else the little troublemaker is good at. In fact, you have significant equity in your home, don't you?"

Charlie nodded, thinking of the frequent letters from his bank and others offering him home equity loans. He could support his family for a long time on what he could borrow in that manner if he had to.

"The next three scenarios measured your response to anxiety." Dr. Connors pulled a form from his desk drawer, stuck it on the clipboard, and scribbled a few notes. "Anxiety is the mortal foe of creative thinking and decisive action. A mind that is clouded with anxiety conjures up all sorts of fears which paralyze your initiative. Fear is the most malignant of all emotions. Your own fears can create a prison more confining than any iron bars. Let's see how you did."

Connors looked back at his clipboard. "When the mind is full of anxiety, memories of past failures loom large and seem likely to be repeated, while past successes seem diminished and unlikely to repeat themselves. When I asked you to put yourself in a state of acute anxiety and then to remember something from your college days, what was your first memory?"

"Failing calculus," Charlie responded.

Dr. Connors nodded, and asked, "You have a lot of wonderful memories from college, don't you?" Charlie smiled, seeing images flash by: meeting Pam in the library, being elected president of the Entrepreneurship Club, even delivering pizza in his old beat up Honda.

"If, instead of asking you to experience anxiety, I had put you in a frame of mind that was at peace and full of courage and confidence, you would have selected one of those other, more positive memories as your first choice. When you're anxious, the little troublemaker becomes like a rabbit frozen in the headlights of fear. He dredges up memories of past failures to frighten you out of taking any risk. The unfortunate paradox is that only by taking some risk will you ever alleviate the root cause of your anxiety."

"The second thing that happens is that the anxious mind distorts your perception of current reality. When you're paralyzed by fear, your problems always seem bigger than they really are, while your own resources seem to shrink away. When I asked you who you thought the other candidate was for the job you wanted you immediately came up with Jeremy Potts. Why was that, Charlie?"

Charlie shrugged.

"Can you think of anyone, anyone at all, who you would less rather be stacked up against in the competition for a job than Jeremy Potts?"

Charlie shook his head. "Nobody. He's the best. He could walk into any job he wanted."

"So why assume Jeremy? Why not Elmer Fudd or Mr. Magoo or Dilbert? Surely you know people who are down at that capacity level, don't you?"

Charlie smiled, broadly this time. "Absolutely. In fact, I used to work with quite a few people like that."

"And what if I told you the job you had applied for was assistant librarian over at the college, rather than being the high-powered executive job I think you probably had in mind. How would Jeremy do in that job?"

"He'd go berserk the first week, with no enemies to conquer and no troops to lead."

"And what if you got that job, at least as something temporary. How would you do?"

"Actually, John," Charlie used the first name without even thinking about it. "I'd love it. Two things I love are good books and being left alone to do my own work, and that job would provide both."

"So any library board that hired Jeremy instead of you would be making a grievous mistake, right?"

"In that case, yes."

"Between now and the next time we get together, Charlie, why don't you try assuming things in your favor? Assume a field that plays to your strengths and desires, not someone else's, and see if that doesn't give you a different — a bigger and brighter — picture of your own future."

"Which brings me to the third anxiety scenario. When you are under anxiety's thumb, you close your eyes to opportunities right in front of you. When you had to have a job or risk losing your home, all you could think of were menial jobs — jobs that would not challenge or reward you."

"But you told me I had to have a job right away," Charlie protested.

"Yes, I did," replied the doctor. "And how long would it have taken for you to go down to Kinko's and have them make up business cards for Charlie McKeever, president of McKeever Enterprises?"

"That wouldn't have worked!"

"Why not? Many of my clients do exactly that. They make up business cards, but have no idea what their business will do until they sign up their first customer. And guess what, Charlie? They usually end up with more money and security than the people who take jobs they don't like."

"The hardest job in the world, Charlie, is to see life as it really is. You've got to break out of what I call the Iron Triangle of False Personality — Ego, Emotion, and Ambition — before you can become the authentic meant-to-be you. But that has to wait for another time, because my appointments are going to start backing up if I don't move along here."

Charlie stood up and extended his hand. "Thanks, John. You've really given me some things to think about."

"That's good, Charlie. Let me give you one more — sort of the ultimate paradox that I feel you will soon confront face-to-face. Your success depends upon your ability to first see and accept life as it really is, but then at the same time to expect the miracle that will be necessary to change your life into what you want it to be as you create your own future."

"Now there's a thought," exclaimed Charlie. "Creating my own future!"

"I don't think we'll need much longer."

CHARLIE MCKEEVER'S KEY LESSONS:

1. Someone with a job is never secure; someone with a calling is never unemployed.

2. See the world as it really is:
   a. Not as it used to be
   b. Not as you wish it were
   c. Not as you fear it might be

3. Anxiety is the mortal foe of creative thinking and decisive action

2

KNOW WHO YOU ARE, WHAT YOU WANT, AND HOW YOU'RE GOING TO GET IT

"WHAT DO YOU DO?"

The question was innocent enough. Charlie had answered it thousands of times: "I'm a senior consultant with Logistics Precision. We're a management consulting firm that helps businesses become more profitable by developing effective competitive strategies." The words were even printed on the back of his business card. Until now, he'd never realized the extent to which he had relied upon his business card to double as an identity card.

Charlie and Pam were at a fundraiser for the local symphony, which had been his wife's favorite charity for many years. So far, he'd been successful at staying off to the side of the room, but now an elegant older woman, wearing more gold than even the most successful dentist would mold in a lifetime, asked, "What do you do?" Charlie kicked himself for not anticipating the question.

"I'm, well, I'm between jobs right now, " he stammered. "I'm looking at..."

She cut him off with a condescending pat on the arm. "How interesting, dear." She was already looking past Charlie to see who else was in the room. "I'm sure something will come up." And she walked off.

Charlie was mortified. "I'm sure something will come up!" As if he was just sitting around all day, waiting for something to happen! Who did she think she was, anyway, to write him off as being unworthy of conversation simply because he was "between jobs?"

"Well, what did you and Madam Butterfly discuss in your little corner?" Pam glided up and took his arm. Short and spunky, she was his counterweight, buoying him up when he was in danger of sinking, and keeping him grounded when he was about to buy a one-way ticket on a flight of fancy.

"Madam Butterfly?"

"That was Wanda Wilmington. She's been chair of the symphony society for, oh, the past eighty years or so. How much did she get you to pledge?"

"Me? Hah! The minute I told her I was unemployed she disappeared faster than your father used to when Nathan needed his diaper changed."

Pam laughed. "Yes, that would be the Madam Butterfly I've come to know and love. Her time is for sale to the highest bidder, or should I say to the highest donor. She can be pretty ruthless, but without her the symphony would have folded years ago."

"I felt absolutely stark naked. She asked me what I did, and I couldn't answer. It's like nothing else mattered, only my job description."

Dr. Connors looked at Charlie and waited for him to say something else. When the silence continued he asked, "What if, instead of asking you what you do, this Madam Butterfly had asked, 'Who are you?'

How would you have responded? Who are you, Charlie McKeever?"

Charlie looked toward the window. Though he hadn't noticed it before, he now heard what sounded like a small army of kids splashing in the pool. Charlie smiled, realizing that right now it felt as if his little troublemaker had invited an army of friends into his mental swimming pool.

"Why don't we start with an easier question." Dr. Connors broke the silence. "Who are you not?" Charlie didn't respond, so Dr. Connors continued. "Let's start with the easiest answer first. You are not your possessions. It should go without saying, but the fact is that most people make their first impression of you on the basis of the clothes you wear, the car you drive, or the country club you belong to. Isn't that what Madam Butterfly did? As soon as she suspected your wallet was empty, you stopped being a real person in her eyes, didn't you?"

Charlie nodded. "The second thing you are not, but which other people want to distill you into, is your job. That's a tougher one because even you will often link your identity with what you do for a living. Occupation and self-worth are closely intertwined, especially in our culture. That's why the question you recently looked forward to answering is now one you dread. 'What do you do?' and 'Who are you?' are almost the same question. Am I right?"

Charlie started to nod yes, but his chin seemed to get stuck on the downward swig. He looked at the floor, and was again fighting back tears. At the age of thirty-six, had he become so superficial that his whole identity could be captured on the back of a business card?

"You're at a crossroads, Charlie. You're about to make a decision that could determine the course of the rest of your life."

"Up to this point in your life you've tried to do what was expected of you and to be the person you thought others expected you to be. You've never really stopped to ask the question, 'What should I do to please and impress Charlie?' have you?"

Charlie wasn't trying to stop the tears now. He shook his head. "No."

"Did you hear about the aborigine who bought a new boomerang?" Dr. Connors laughed. Charlie shook his head. "Spent the rest of his life trying to throw the old one away."

Charlie laughed through his tears.

"That's the question, Charlie. Are you ready to throw away the old boomerang, and to keep throwing it away every time it comes back to you? The old boomerang is trying to do what you think will please and impress everyone else, even if it makes you unhappy; playing it safe by staying close to the ground when deep in your heart you want to spread your wings and soar, even if at first it's terrifying to fly? Are you ready, Charlie, or do you want to hang on to the old boomerang for a while longer?"

"I think I'm ready," Charlie replied, "but I'm not sure I'd even know where to start."

"I won't kid you by saying it's easy, Charlie, but you've already made a critical first step."

"What's that?"

"You recognize that the boomerang is not part of you, that it's something you can throw away and replace, if you want to."

"I want to."

"Remember last time we were together, when I mentioned The Iron Triangle of False Personality? It's rounded on each corner by ego, emotion, and ambition. Now, each of those things is good if you manage them by staying outside of the triangle. But most people don't manage them. They are run by them. When they are trapped inside the triangle, it becomes a prison that prevents their development as human beings and as spiritual beings."

Charlie looked up, a bit surprised. "Is religion compatible with psychiatry?"

"Your religion — the church you attend, or don't attend — is your own business. But as long as I'm your counselor, your spiritual life is my business. 'Who are you?' is ultimately a spiritual question, because when you break out of the Iron Triangle what you find on the other side is soul."

"The first point of the Iron Triangle is ego. I don't mean ego in the technical sense that Freud described, but rather in the everyday sense you think of when you hear that someone has a big ego, or a fragile ego. It's the embodiment of that trouble-making little kid, whose primary concern is other people's opinions. It was ego that got crushed when Madam Butterfly gave you the brush-off. It's ego that still nurses the hurt feelings rather than letting them go. You've probably heard reference to your inner child? Well, ego can be your inner spoiled brat."

"If ego stands in the way of my discovering soul, then how do I distinguish between the two? Sometimes, it's awfully hard to know just exactly who's talking up there."

"Great question, Charlie, and one I can't answer directly. Let's finish our analysis of The Iron Triangle and see if we can't get a little closer to the answer."

"Ego is the great defender. Its primary purpose is to protect you from being hurt by the outside world, but in doing that it prevents you from touching the outside world in more positive and constructive ways. It was ego that slammed the door in Dick Dierdron's face when he was offering to help you. It may have felt good at the time, but knowing that someday Dierdron might be an important job reference for you, it was a counterproductive behavior, don't you think?"

Charlie was starting to get a better appreciation for what Dr. Connors had said earlier. Gaining control of the little troublemaker was the hardest work in the world because it *still* felt good to have closed that door in Dierdron's face, even knowing that he might someday pay a regrettable price.

"When ego wants to get your attention," Dr. Connors began again, "it has a very handy chain to yank — your emotions. Emotions can be a beautiful thing. They make humans unique, but often they are also the enemy within. Ego loves to stir up emotions that make it feel important, but which can provoke you into doing things that end up being self-destructive."

Dr. Connors filled up a big glass of water and put it on his desk. "When ego starts stirring up emotions, it rarely hits on just one. What you often end up with is a confused witches' brew."

Connors tapped the glass. "Crystal clear, like the swimming pool before it was disrupted by our little troublemaker. A mind this clear would be a perfect environment for making decisions with clarity, do you agree?"

Charlie nodded.

"When Dick Dierdron fired you, it was excruciatingly painful to your ego, wasn't it?" Charlie nodded again as his stomach started to knot. "Your ego started to stir up emotions, didn't it? What were they, Charlie? What were some of the emotions you felt that day?"

Charlie clenched his teeth. "Anger," he hissed.

"Ah, good old anger," chortled Dr. Connors as he pulled a small bottle out of his desk and removed the top. "Favorite emotion of Mars, the Greek god of war. Bloody red anger." He squeezed several drops of red food dye into the water. "Nothing better to cloud your thinking than anger." Charlie was mesmerized by the red dye as it swirled its way through the water, fighting a losing battle to maintain its separate identity.

"What other emotions did you feel that afternoon?" "Fear," Charlie replied. "Sheer terror, total panic, heart-stopping fear."

"Fear and anger. Never one without the other," Dr. Connors said as he squeezed several drops of yellow dye into the water. Charlie watched as the red and yellow, each pretty on its own, melded together into a murky orange. "What else did you feel as you sat in Dierdron's office, knowing that when the meeting ended you would go and he would stay?"

"Envy. At that moment, I think I would have given anything to trade places with him."

"Ah, so let's add a little envy to the brew," Connors said as he squirted green food coloring into the glass, causing the water to turn a dark purple. "And what about Dierdron himself, what emotion did you feel toward him?"

"Hate. Pure unadulterated hatred." Charlie shuddered "It was actually scary to feel that much animosity towards another person, especially one I had considered a friend just hours before."

Dr. Connors squeezed some purple dye into to the concoction on his desk, then stirred it up with his pen. It looked like India ink. Connors picked up the glass and held it out toward Charlie. "Care to drink some of your brew?"

Charlie recoiled at the thought of tasting the vile-looking concoction.

"This is what happens to your mental clarity when ego starts to stir up all those negative emotions. It goes," Connors said as he poured the contents of the glass into the sink, "down the drain."

"So now you're in a mess, aren't you, Charlie? You have a wounded ego stirring up all sorts of painful emotions. How do you deal with that, huh? I'll tell you how. You focus on your ambitions."

Connors was pacing back and forth, more animated than Charlie had ever seen him. "Your fear is painful, so you give yourself a goal to find another job as quickly as possible to reduce the frightening uncertainty of being unemployed. You hate Dierdron, so you think of ways to get back at him."

Charlie squirmed uncomfortably. He had, in fact, been daydreaming about taking critical business away from LPI, and more recently had even begun to sketch out a business plan for doing so.

"Here's the sad fact. None of those ambitions are authentic. They are intended to placate ego, and to please and impress other people."

They sat in silence. At last, Dr. Connors pulled a book from his shelf and handed it to Charlie. "This is *The Self-Transformation Workbook*, which many of my clients have found to be helpful in trying to get a better handle on who they are and what they want."

Charlie took the book and pointed to the Never Fear, Never Quit logo at the top. "I see this on T-shirts all over the place. I didn't realize it was more than a slogan."

"I was one of the first members," Dr. Connors smiled. "The movement has come a long way."

Charlie started to thumb through the workbook. "Your friend Cheryl told me she locked herself into her room with that book and didn't come out until she had worked her way through it, from beginning to end," Dr. Connors said. "Judging from what she's done with her life since, I'd say it's made quite an impression."

"I really need to call Cheryl again," Charlie said. "The fragile state of my ego prevented me from really connecting the last time."

"Cheryl has a lot to offer, Charlie. She's going to make a difference in this world."

Dr. Connors went back to his shelf and pulled off another book. Charlie recognized it as the *Dreamcyclopedia* Cheryl had taken from her purse, but this one did not yet have anything in it. "Here's a blank slate, Charlie. Go fill it up with a beautiful future."

If anything, this day was even more beautiful than the first day Charlie had met Cheryl for lunch at dockside on The Patio. This time Charlie felt sunshine on the inside as well as on the outside. Charlie noticed immediately that a second jewel now graced one of the indentations in Cheryl's FPN pin.

"Future Perfect Now," Cheryl said, "means just what it says. Instead of waiting around, hoping that a brighter future will somehow happen, we reach out and grab that future, start living it now as if it were already a reality."

"OK, I believe you Cheryl—you are a living, breathing billboard — but what exactly is FPN? What do you do?"

Cheryl smiled and shook her head no. "You're not ready yet, Charlie. Your dreams are still too small. Until you can let go of them and replace them with big dreams, Mount Everest-sized dreams, it would be worse than a waste of time to tell you about it. You'd blow it off and never come back, and that would really be a shame."

"Well," Charlie replied, "you said that there was something you wanted to walk through with me today. If it's not Future Perfect Now, what is it?"

"This will take most of the afternoon, Charlie, but if you're willing to take the time, it could change your life in a radical, beautiful way, like it has mine. Are you willing?"

"Ready, willing and able... and eager!"

Cheryl unfolded a long sheet of paper with six empty blocks, each progressively smaller, forming a pyramid. "This is the EMPOWERMENT PYRAMID," she said. "It's a powerful tool for figuring out who you are, what you want, and how you're going to get it."

"Starting at the beginning, with IDENTITY at the base of the pyramid, we'll use this tool to crystallize your identity, mission, vision, goals, and then the action steps you can start taking right now to make sure that your future is the perfect one you want it to be."

Underneath the word Identity, Cheryl wrote out in longhand "Authenticity," and then the numbers one, two, and three. "Crystallizing your identity means to discover the real you, the meant-to-be you, the authentic you that has probably long been overshadowed by the false you that ego has created to please and impress other people." Charlie could hear echoes of Dr. Connors in Cheryl's voice, but also sensed that she was about to tell him something new and different.

"There are three steps to cultivating your authentic identity. First, know yourself. Second, master yourself. Third, believe in yourself. Since you've spent some time with John Connors, I don't need to tell you about The Iron Triangle and how important it is to cut through that clutter, to have the courage to be the person you are meant to be."

She checked to see that Charlie was with her, then continued, "One of the most effective methods for defining your true identity is 'I Am' declarations. I've written one for myself at three different levels — spiritual, professional, and personal. Would you like to see them?"

Charlie nodded and she opened her *Dreamcyclopedia* and read aloud:

> *I am a beloved and beautiful child of God, and have been put on this Earth with an important mission that I alone can fulfill. That mission will be made clear to me as I continue to work and grow, but so long as I am pursuing it with enthusiasm and good faith, I will not be allowed to fail, no matter how severe the obstacles may seem.*

"Whenever someone asks me that universal icebreaking question, 'What do you do?' I tell them about my work with FPN, because that's what they expect to hear. But when I see the looks of disapproval, which is fairly often because FPN is pretty far off the beaten path, I remind myself of this 'I Am...' declaration. No matter what someone thinks of my work, they can never take this away from me. It's not a job, it's a calling." Cheryl uncovered the middle third of the page, and read her professional 'I Am' declaration:

> *I am a natural-born entrepreneur, and I love nothing better than helping other people grow wealthy and wise right alongside me.*

"This one sentence is my entire business philosophy," Cheryl said. "Wealth is not enough without wisdom. My own success is not enough without the success of those around me. I must be creating something of unique and lasting value — the hallmark of an entre-preneur. Whenever I get discouraged — when I've been rejected too often, dejected for too long, and being ejected altogether seems like a real possibility—I center myself on what's most important by mental-ly declaring who I really am: a natural born entrepreneur with a commitment to the success of others." Cheryl lifted the paper from the book, revealing the bottom third of the page. Charlie read:

I am a loving and compassionate wife and mother, and will do whatever I can to help my family be more harmonious and my children be more successful.

Cheryl laughed. "Every time I come in the house and see chaos reigning, chores neglected, homework not done, TV blaring and children fighting, I stop, take a deep breath, and before I follow my first instinct I remind myself of who I am and who I want to be. Guess what? Nine times out of ten, what my first instinct would have led me to do was an inappropriate response. It was ego pulling the strings, not soul."

Charlie pointed to the "I Am" declarations. "I know I'm supposed to write my own, but would you mind if I copy yours ? They sort of hit home."

"Not at all," Cheryl replied. "That's how I got started, by massaging someone else's declarations until they felt right for me."

Next Cheryl wrote the words Master Yourself. "In order to become the authentic you, you need to keep a tight rein on ego, emotions, and ambition. Have you heard about tough love?"

"You mean that 'get tough' philosophy for parents whose kids are into drugs?" Charlie asked.

"Exactly. Well, your ego is like a truculent little kid who's into drugs of a different type. Drugs like self-pity, pessimism, cynicism, and other loser attitudes. And believe me, those negative attitudes and beliefs are just as addictive as narcotics. They suck people into a downward spiral that begins with 'learned helplessness' — pretending there's nothing you can do to solve your problems. Then they swirl downward into the 'blame game' — trying to hold someone other than yourself responsible for those problems. They culminate in 'victim syndrome' — feeling sorry for yourself because you've been singled out for special abuse. And the spiral never ends, because once you feel like a victim, your belief in your own helplessness is reinforced and you continue to spiral down into despair."

"To become the authentic you, you must be tough with yourself by holding yourself accountable for achieving high standards, values, and performance. By the way, being tough *with* yourself doesn't mean being tough *on* yourself by beating yourself up if you don't live up to those high expectations."

"And third," she continued, "you have to believe in yourself. You have to believe, in your heart, that those 'I Am' declarations are true and authentic. After all, if you don't believe in yourself, who will?"

Cheryl now wrote in big block letters the word MISSION in the second box. "Once you've got a clear fix on who you are, the next step is to crystallize what you're here for. When you go from having a job to having a mission, you become unstoppable. One of the most powerfully motivating things you can do for yourself is write a mission statement. Have you ever done that, Charlie?"

Charlie shook his head. "No, but every now and then I read the one posted in the lobby at LPI . It sounded pretty much like every other mission statement, and could just as well have applied to a sausage factory as a consulting firm."

Cheryl turned the page on her *Dreamcyclopedia* and pointed to her own mission statement:

> *My mission is to help people succeed as entrepreneurs*
> *by teaching them how to dream big, think creatively,*
> *believe in their own abilities, and act courageously so*
> *that they can accomplish magnificent goals.*

"If you dissect my mission statement," Cheryl pointed out, "you'll notice three distinct elements. First my guiding value, which is magnificence as opposed to mediocrity. That word captures everything I stand for, personally and professionally — raising people's standards and expectations and achieving quantum leaps in their outcomes.

"The second element is teaching. Teaching people how to be successful entrepreneurs is more central to my success than being a successful entrepreneur myself."

Charlie realized that their waitress was looking over his shoulder at Cheryl's dream book. Red-faced at being caught eavesdropping, she stammered, "Sorry, I just came over to check and got taken in listening. I sure don't want to be a waitress for the rest of my life."

"What are you doing right now to try and get out of that rut, Sarah?" Cheryl asked, reading the woman's nametag.

"Well, it's hard to find time," Sarah replied. "I'm a single mom, and my boys are at an age where they pretty much need me to be around. But," and at this point Sarah lowered her voice as if she were bringing Cheryl and Charlie into a conspiracy, "I've been taking this home study course on how to think like an entrepreneur, and it's really opened my eyes to the possibilities out there. If I'm still waitressing in five years, it will only be because I made that choice."

Sarah looked uncertainly from Cheryl to Charlie. "One of the assignments my teacher — the guy who does this home study course — gives is to start a new business doing something we've never done before, and to keep at it until we've grossed at least one hundred dollars. When Charlie raised his eyebrows at the token amount, she snapped. It's a lot harder than you think it is!"

"So what are you doing to earn your hundred dollars?" Cheryl broke in genuinely interested.

Sarah looked around to make sure she wasn't being watched by a supervisor, then reached into the pocket of her apron and pulled out a round pin. It was hand-painted, clearly done by someone with talent. In the middle was the head of a bald eagle, and around the circumference the words, *Winners Don't Quit!*

"That's my motto," Sarah said proudly. "I'm a winner, and winners don't quit. Working at this job, I have to remind myself of that pretty often."

Charlie caught himself looking at the young woman with new respect. It was funny, he thought, how something as simple as trying to sell hand-painted inspirational buttons transformed a generic waitress into a person with dreams and aspirations. "How much do you sell the pins for?" he asked.

"Well, sir," she replied, "if price is your most important concern you can get buttons down at Target for about two bucks. If you want a work of art like this that you'll be proud to wear wherever you go, the price is ten dollars." Her eyes never wavered from Charlie's during the entire speech.

After a brief silence, Cheryl started laughing. "How long did you have to practice that so you could pull it off with a straight face?"

"Lady," Sarah replied, "you don't even want to know how many hours I stood in front of the bathroom mirror 'til I felt I could ask for what they're worth. That's one thing the teacher for this home study course really hammers home. You have to rehearse great answers to simple questions like, 'What do you do?' and 'How much does it cost?'"

Charlie took a ten-dollar bill from his wallet and handed it to Sarah. "After a sales pitch like that, how can I not buy a pin? I'd also like to know where I can sign up for this home study course you mentioned, if you don't mind giving me a phone number or address."

Sarah handed Charlie the pin, then turned to Cheryl. "I've got another one pretty much like it, if you'd like one too."

"Actually, Sarah, I need 150 of them. But I need them for a special function on September 22. Can you make them that fast?"

"At ten dollars a pin?" Sarah asked.

Cheryl smiled and nodded. "You certainly don't need to worry about being a waitress for the rest of your life, Sarah. Ten bucks a pin, but on one condition."

"What condition?"

"This sale doesn't go against your quota. You still have to sell at least ninety dollars worth of pins to someone else to satisfy your homework assignment. Here's my card. Why don't you give me a call next week so we can talk more about what goes on the pin."

Sarah put the card in her pocket. "These pins are going to be perfect, you have my guarantee of that." Sarah turned to go, then looked back at Cheryl. "By the way, I'm already way past my hundred dollar quota. See you next week."

Cheryl started to say something to Charlie, then stopped. "Hey, what happened to your pin?"

"It's in my pocket."

"What's it doing in there? Don't you want people to know you're a winner?"

Charlie fished the pin out and put it on. "OK, it's on. So where were we?"

"Actually," Cheryl said, "Sarah came at just the right time, because she is the third element of my mission statement."

"Excuse me, did I miss something?"

"The first element is my guiding value — magnificence over mediocrity. The second element is my critical action step — teaching people the skills and attitudes for success. The third element is my intended audience, and that is people who have big dreams and want to achieve them on their own terms. People like Sarah."

"People who want the future to be perfect right now?" Charlie asked.

"Precisely. And I predict that I'm going to help Sarah sell a lot more than 150 pins to my friends in FPN, if that's what she really wants to do. But also that she's going to end up doing a lot to help me succeed in my own business." Cheryl smiled. "I knew she had what it takes as soon as I saw her look you right in the eye and tell you that the price was ten bucks, take it or leave it."

Returning to the Empowerment Pyramid, Cheryl now put big block letters in the third box spelling out the word VISION. "What would your world look like if you were being the real you, the authentic you, and pursuing the work that is your true calling? What work would you be doing every day? Where would you be doing it? With whom? Where would you live? In what kind of house? The more clear and detailed the mental map of your perfect future, the more certain you are to take the actions now that will assure it becomes your reality."

Cheryl sketched an hourglass on the side of the paper. "This is the way future vision works." She drew a straight line across the bottom of the hourglass. "This is the present. My vision of reality is very broad, very accurate. I can tell you precisely about the work I'm doing, the house I live in, anything else you want to know."

She drew a second line, parallel to the first but closer to the middle. "This line is tomorrow. I still have a very clear and accurate picture of where I am going to be and what I am going to be doing, but it's just a bit narrower than it is today, because there's a hint of uncertainty thrown in, isn't there?" Charlie nodded. "Now, if I go out a week or a month," and she drew two more lines, each fractionally closer to the midpoint, "my vision becomes even more circumscribed, and still more if I go out a year, or two years."

"At some point," and she drew a line straight across the narrow waist of the hourglass, "there is a great deal of uncertainty, because so many things are beyond our control. Somewhere out here, maybe three to five years, I can't tell you with a great deal of confidence where I will be and what I will be doing."

Cheryl drew a line perpendicular to the horizontal one at the bottom of the hourglass, then put an arrowhead at the end so that it pointed toward the opposite side. "But if you give me enough time — and I happen to think there's something magic about seven years — I can begin to have complete certainty that I'll be doing what I want to do, where I want to do it, and with the kind of people I want to be doing it with."

"That's the paradox of memories of the future, Charlie. You can be far more certain of your reality in the distant future than you can for the intervening five years or so, if you're willing to keep working, keep adjusting, and not quit," and she tapped Charlie's new eagle pin with her pen.

"Memories of the future?" Charlie asked.

"That's an FPN technique. We don't have time to go into the details right now, but basically it's a mental motion picture of your ideal future"

"Wow!" Charlie drew out the word to emphasize how impressed he was. "You really are taking this business seriously, aren't you?"

"If I just take whatever life tosses my way, and then one day wake up and decide I want more, will I be given the chance to do it over again?"

"No, of course not."

"You're darned right I'm taking it seriousl! I want magnificence, not mediocrity! There are too many things I want to do in this life. Which brings me to the next block of the Empowerment Pyramid," and she wrote GOALS into the next empty box.

"Goals are the stepping stones that take you from where you are now to where you want to be in your perfect future. At FPN, we talk about the two possible impossibilities."

Charlie laughed. "First memories of the future and now possible impossibilities?"

Cheryl smiled like a mother trying to be tolerant when a child has asked "Why?" about ten times too often. "The difference between courageous and crazy is often evident only in retrospect. It takes a lot of courage to commit yourself to a vision of a beautiful future, especially when everyone else thinks it's just an impossible daydream."

"I'm sorry," said Charlie. "My thinking has been stuck in the corporate box too long."

"You mean your dreams have been too small," Cheryl said. "But at least I see the beginning of a crack at the top of that box. Maybe you're about to break out."

"Crazier things have happened."

"Let's hope so. The first possible impossibility is to have one magnificent dream, one goal that is so stupendous that other people think it's impossible."

"I remember reading once that lost causes are the only ones worth fighting for," Charlie said, and just then the picture of Mt. Everest in

Dick Dierdron's office popped into his head, with its inscription 'Big Hills are the Only Ones Worth Climbing.'

"The second possible impossibility," Cheryl continued, "is to have an impossible number of possible goals. To write down everything you'd like to do, all the places you'd like to go, the people you'd like to meet. You'll find that when you start getting these goals organized the seemingly impossible becomes inevitable, and your goals start becoming fulfilled in big clusters. I know, because it's starting to happen to me right now, in my business and in my personal life. I'm achieving goals I 'never' would have thought to strive for if I hadn't written them down."

"One more thing about goals," Cheryl went on. "Whenever you begin an activity, have more than one goal in mind so that your likelihood of success is higher."

"I'm not sure I'm with you on that one," Charlie said. "Can you give me an example?"

"Sure," Cheryl replied. "Let's say you go somewhere for a job interview. What's your objective?"

"To get the job, of course. What else would it be?"

"If that's your only objective going in," Cheryl responded, "you're setting yourself up for a win-or-lose outcome. If you get the job you win — well, you win if it actually turns out to be what you're hoping it will be. But if you don't get the job, you feel like you've lost, because you didn't achieve your sole objective."

"If, on the other hand, getting the job is only one of several objectives, you set yourself up to win, no matter what the outcome is. You might not get the job, but you'll achieve your other objectives of learning more about the industry, getting names and telephone numbers of other people you can network with, and analyzing how your resume and your interview skills might have been more effective at helping you land the job. With all that to gain, you're a winner no matter what happens."

"Easy to say," Charlie replied, "but it's still hard to feel like a winner when you've been rejected."

"Look, I have a friend who's a writer. He told me that he used to get really depressed whenever he went to a book signing. Because he's not a household name, most people just walk by his table. He felt like he was being rejected by all of the people who didn't want his book. But now he has multiple objectives at each signing. He asks the store manager for tips on how to market his books more effectively. He signs up new subscribers for his newsletter. And when people do stop, he engages them in conversations, asking about what they do and what their problems are. By doing that, he told me, he's always a winner. In fact, one evening when he signed only a few books turned out to be one of his best outings because someone who did buy the book ended up hiring him several months later for a big consulting project. And as part of the deal, he bought more than a thousand books for employees of the company!"

"And that brings me to the apex of the pyramid," she said and blocked the word ACTION in the box at the top. "You can have all the beautiful dreams in the world, but they will only come true if you are willing to make the commitments and take the actions necessary to make them come true. The difference between wishful thinking and positive thinking is this: wishful thinking is hoping for something and waiting for it to happen, but positive thinking is *expecting* something and *working* for it to happen."

Charlie studied the Empowerment Pyramid. It really could, he realized, be a formula for finding out who you are, what you want, and how you're going to get it. "There's one more thing," said Cheryl, "and it's very important. Once you realize what your dreams and visions really are, you have to give yourself permission to follow those dreams, to become the person you were meant to be. You have to stop doing what you think the rest of the world expects you to do. The bigger your dream, and the more it requires you to change, the less likely it will be that other people, including people who love and support you, are going to understand. Above all, you've got to believe in yourself and in your dreams before you can expect anyone else to."

Charlie contemplated what Cheryl had just said. To move from completing the Empowerment Pyramid on paper to making a real, here-and-now commitment, would require extraordinary courage and determination.

The after-work crowd was starting to filter into The Patio when Cheryl excused herself for an early evening appointment. Charlie started making notes for his own *Dreamcyclopedia.*

THE EMPOWERMENT PYRAMID:

Identity
1. Know yourself
2. Master yourself
3. Believe in yourself

Mission
1. Guiding value
2. Key action to make guiding value real
3. Intended audience

Vision
1. Present
2. Near Future
3. Distant Future

Goals

Action

3

Dream a Big Dream,
Make It a Memory of the Future,
and Expect a Miracle

Charlie had never been this nervous before a meeting, not even one of the "paydirt presentations" at Logistics Precision, where his performance might make the difference between landing a big contract or landing in hot water. It was funny, he thought, because no contract or job offer would come from the meeting with Alan Silvermane. He was long retired and was meeting with Charlie as a favor to a friend.

"Most people don't want to be winners, because winning would be inconsistent with their self-image of being survivors or victims." Charlie read that in an interview *Forbes* magazine had conducted several years earlier with Silvermane as part of their annual story on America's wealthiest people. Silvermane had ranked twenty-fifth that year. "Not bad for a kid who climbed down the steps of a boat from Europe in a rainstorm without even an umbrella," he had commented.

"In my experience," Silvermane told *Forbes*, "most of the people in this country see themselves as survivors. They'll make it through whatever the world throws at them, and if things get too bad, there's always somewhere they can run to and make a fresh start." Silvermane had accurately described Charlie's emotional reaction to losing the job.

"Then there are the victims," Silvermane said. "They can never seem to rise above their problems. Victims are stuck in boring jobs, toxic relationships, bankrupt finances." Charlie smiled, recognizing himself in this description as well.

"That leaves a small percentage of the population — the winners who refuse to be made victims and who aspire to more than merely surviving — to carry the burden of creating wealth and progress."

Charlie reviewed the questions he wanted to ask Silvermane — mainly questions about dreaming big. "If my dreams are too small," he'd asked Cheryl, "then how do I learn to dream big?" She thought for a moment, then replied, "A friend of mine named Marv Johnston knows Alan Silvermane. You know, the guy who started the B-A-R corporation when he was twenty-four and forty years later sold it for more than 500 million dollars. When it comes to thinking big, he wrote the book. I'll see if I can make a connection for you."

The connection had been made and now Charlie was sitting in Alan Silvermane's living room. It was nice, but nothing about it suggested it was the home of one of America's most wealthy businessmen. Silvermane had even answered his own door. Charlie had anticipated a butler.

They'd been speaking for almost an hour, and Charlie had yet to ask a question. The older man wanted to know everything about his guest. Charlie was having a hard time believing that the interest was real, that this billionaire would really care about his employment history, family, and hobbies (and then he immediately reminded himself to watch the negative self-talk). But Silvermane's attention never wavered. If anything, he seemed to be taking Charlie more seriously than Charlie took himself.

At length Silvermane leaned back in his chair and said, "So far I've done all the talking. Where do you want to start?"

The eloquent opening lines Charlie had so carefully rehearsed had long since evaporated into the flow of conversation "I'm not sure," he said. "Cheryl von Noyes tells me that my dreams are too small, that I've been cheating myself by pretending to be satisfied with some pretty anemic goals. I suppose she's right. I'd fall somewhere between thinking of myself as a survivor and a victim on your scale."

"Where do you *want* to fall on that scale, Charlie?" Silvermane asked. "It takes a lot of commitment, hard work, and sacrifice to move yourself up, but when you see the view from the top, you'll be thankful you made the climb."

"The first problem, Mr. Silvermane, is that I'm not really sure I want to climb a mountain at all. I guess I've gotten complacent hanging around down here in the valley and sort of look at myself as being too old to take up rock climbing. And if I decided I wanted to climb a mountain, I don't have a clue which one I'd choose."

"Build your castles in the air, where they belong. Then put foundations under them. Thoreau said that. I can't help you with the first question, Charlie. Whether or not you can is between you and God. But maybe I can help you with the second, because when it comes to deciding which mountain you wish to climb, or which castle to build, there are some general guiding principles."

Silvermane walked over to a shelf and pulled down a fat notebook, which he opened to a page that was marked with a post-it note.

"My friend John Marks Templeton is widely known, not only as a brilliant financial thinker, but also as a man whose unbridled optimism is fueled by a powerful faith in the hand of God working in this world. So when he predicted, back in 1992..." and here, Silvermane read from what appeared to be a newsletter stored in the binder, "that the Dow Jones Industrial Average may have reached six thousand, perhaps more, by the beginning of the 21st century, not very many people took him seriously. Most wrote it off as the wishful thinking of an incorrigible optimist."

Silvermane sat down with the notebook in his lap, and Charlie could see words and numbers scribbled all along the margins. "Do you follow the stock market, Charlie?"

"Not really," he replied.

"Well, if you did you would know that the Dow surpassed the ten-thousand mark a year before Sir John so optimistically predicted six-thousand, and then kept on going higher."

"I'm telling you this, Charlie, because in many ways it's a metaphor for the decisions you face. Over the long term, the upside potential is always much greater than the downside risk. If you had invested one thousand dollars in a mutual fund that simply tracked the Dow back in 1992, it would be worth more than three thousand dollars today. But even under the worst case scenario — say the market were to plunge fifty percent — the most you would have lost would be five hundred dollars or so."

"That's the first of three paradoxes that occur when you set your sights on a big goal, one that ordinary people think of as impossible. What you stand to gain is so far out of proportion to what you might lose that even if you fail the first time, or the first ten times, if you keep at it the payback always comes. And here's the kicker: the downside risk is usually the same no matter what the upside potential. You have to pledge your house to the bank to start a million dollar business or a hundred million dollar business, but you can only lose that house one time, right?"

Silvermane got up again and returned the notebook to the shelf. "The second paradox is that audacious goals are more likely, not less likely, to be achieved than timid little ones. I'm a big supporter of Habitat for Humanity. Are you familiar with the organization?"

"More than I am with the stock market," Charlie replied with a smile.

"Well, you know that Millard Fuller, the man who started it all, has this seemingly impossible goal of eradicating poverty housing everywhere in the world. That's quite a stretch, when you consider that there are over one billion people — more than three times the population of the United States — who are inadequately housed. But you know what? In its first 23 years, Habitat built more that 80,000 homes, and it will take fewer than five years for them to build the next 80,000. On that trajectory, you can actually see the day where the impossible dream of yesterday will be the reality of tomorrow."

"Now, where do you suppose Fuller would be if instead of targeting poverty housing around the world, he had decided to start in his home state of Georgia, conquer the problem there, and then move on to South Carolina and so forth. Where would he be today?"

"Still in Georgia?"

"Precisely. It was the magnificence, the grandeur of the dream that propelled his efforts forward, that attracted the very resources necessary for the dream's fulfillment. If people only knew! Do you think Millard Fuller is working 80,000 times harder than the well-intentioned social worker who spends a month trying to find decent housing for one family?"

"No, of course not."

"Wanna know the third paradox?" Charlie nodded and Silvermane went on. "Audacious goals, castle in the sky dreams, are never just achieved. They are always transcended. They become the platform for bigger and better dreams, for the higher mountain in the distance that only becomes visible after you've peaked the ones in the foreground."

"Back in the early '50s I was doing some work for Walt Disney. Talk about a big dreamer! Well, one day I was in his office and he was having a conversation with his brother Roy, who was sort of Walt's managerial counterweight. Walt was all excited about how wonderful this new theme park of his was going to be, but Roy looked like he'd just sat on a porcupine. Walt was seeing fairy castles in the air, and Roy was seeing a big hole in the ground into which he would have to pour their hard-earned money. At one point, he got real exasperated and just said, 'Walt, why can't you let go of this impossible dream for Disneyland and concentrate on making some money in the movie business?'"

Silvermane smiled. "Well, of course we know what happened. Not only was Disneyland not an impossible dream, it wasn't even a particularly big dream, was it? Why, closing Disneyland tomorrow would hardly put a dent in the balance sheet of the worldwide entertainment empire that started with the dreams of one man."

"Yeah, but big dreams cost a lot of money." Charlie's troublemaker was finally able to say something in this conversation.

"I'll tell you another paradox," Silvermane replied. "I've known some very big dreamers, very successful dreamers. Not one of them dreamed of money. Their dreams were always bigger than money. And not one of them worried about money. They had faith that the money they needed at each step would be there for them when they needed it. When you worry about where the money is coming from, you start to poison the dream."

Charlie nodded. "A friend of mine likes to say that worry is ingratitude to God — in advance."

"You have a very wise friend." Silvermane refilled the teacups. "You know what one of my big dreams is? To have a cup that keeps my tea at just the right temperature without having to wrap it in ugly plastic insulation or to cover it up with a lid with a tiny little sipping hole."

Charlie laughed. "Me too! Several years ago I took a ceramics class at the community college and made some cupholders that have a spot for a little tea candle underneath. They work great!"

Silvermane looked at the younger man, as if gauging the strength of a quality he had not yet detected. "Do you still have some of those cupholders?"

Charlie nodded. "They're not very attractive, but they serve the purpose."

"I wonder if you would send one my way. I'd love to keep my tea warm while I'm reading."

"Sure, no problem. In fact, I can drop one off tomorrow. With my current job, the hours are, you might say, flexible."

Silvermane laughed but his gaze never left Charlie. "Find a need and fill it. That's what Robert Schuller always tells people who have, uhm, flexible hours. And that's what you've done, isn't it?"

"Well, I guess so, yeah."

"It wasn't that difficult, was it?"

Charlie smiled and shook his head. "It was also not a very big need."

"I'll tell you why big ambitious goals are more likely to succeed than timid little ones." Charlie pulled a pen from his suit coat pocket, then looked to Silvermane as if for permission to make notes. "What I'm telling you is vitally important!" The older man exclaimed. "By all means, write it down!"

"A great big goal, a bet-the-company kind of goal, gives you four powerful tools that are not available with timid little goals. First, it's a magnet. When you're committed to a big goal — and I don't just mean it's something that you'd sort of like to do, but with an 'if it kills me' kind of commitment — it's a magnet that attracts the right people, money, and everything else you need for its fulfillment."

"The second tool it gives you is a compass. When you've got your bearings fixed on a big mountain, you're much less likely to be drawn down all the little side paths of temptation."

"Third," he continued, "it's a magnifying glass. We each have only so much time and energy, and when you have a huge goal you learn to focus it the way a magnifying glass pinpoints the sun's rays. You know, the average American spends twenty-five or thirty hours a week sitting in front of the boob tube; more than one third of their so-called free time is wasted on drivel. People with big dreams have more productive ways to engage their imaginations."

"Finally, a big dream is a flywheel. In your car's engine, the function of a flywheel is to maintain the crankshaft's momentum between each piston firing. That's what a big dream does. It keeps you going through the days when your pistons aren't firing, when you've been rejected one time too many, when but for your commitment to that dream it would be so easy to quit." Silvermane chuckled. "To quit and get a real job."

Charlie smiled. He had a feeling that he would someday look back on this afternoon with Alan Silvermane as one of the most important in his life, yet if he'd still been working at LPI, he would never have allowed himself the time.

As if in counterpoint to Charlie's thoughts, Silvermane said, "I hope I'm not boring you. Old fogies like me don't get much chance to share their wisdom."

"Not at all," Charlie responded. "I was actually trying to think of how I can use these tools in my own situation."

"Well," Silvermane replied, "you've got to take your big dreams and transform them into memories of the future. Once you rely on that, your success becomes assured."

Charlie was surprised at the reference. "My friend Cheryl works for a group called Future Perfect Now, and memories of the future are one of the tools they use to motivate their people."

"Yes, I know. The founder of FPN has been, shall we say, a student of mine for a number of years. Memories of the future can be much more tangible and much more reliable than memories of the past. After all, for most of us our memory richly deserves the reputation it has earned for unreliability, doesn't it?"

"Well, yes."

"Let me illustrate. I would like for you to describe to me the events of your second birthday, in every detail. Tell me about the party, the gifts you received, the friends who were there, everything."

Charlie stared back blankly.

"What's the matter, Charlie, you did have a second birthday, didn't you?"

Charlie nodded.

"But you can't remember it! My point exactly. Now, tell me if you can close your eyes and picture where you're going to be in five minutes — who you'll be with, what you'll be wearing, even what you'll be talking about. Can you picture it?"

"Well of course," Charlie replied. "I'll be right here with you."

"Close your eyes and picture it," Silvermane commanded. "Can you see me and the room we're in clearly? Don't open your eyes yet, just concentrate on the picture. Can you see it?" Before he waited for Charlie to answer, Silvermane said, "Now, can you hear in your mind what we're talking about, what my answers are to the questions you're about to ask? Can you hear me saying 'yes' to a request you've made for my help?"

"Sure. I can imagine that."

"You're doing more than imagining, Charlie. You're bringing it about. You have much more influence over the direction of the conversation than you imagine. Now, can you visualize a situation you will be in tomorrow?"

Charlie nodded.

"Next week?"

Another nod.

"Next month? Next year? Five years from now? My experience with highly successful people is that they are very adept at 'remembering' something that will happen in the future, and at being confident their memory is reliable. It gives them a greater store of faith to take necessary risks when they know how the story will turn out."

"Most people think of time as a river flowing by, unstoppable and irreversible. I prefer to think of time as a lake, and my position as something over which I have a reasonable degree of control. I can paddle over to the end of the lake that other people think of as the future and build a dock to receive my boat when I return. I'll mark the path with buoys so that when I come back to the present, I will have a mental roadmap to guide me back to that dock, that memory of the future I've created."

"All of the articles that have been written about me and my business success over the years missed the most important point. Not one of them said I was so successful simply because I knew where I was going, and I knew where I was going because I'd already been there. I guess their left-brained readers would have thought it was too weird, which is too bad, because it really works. Do you want to know how it works?"

"Yes, I do." Charlie answered, anxious to learn how to use a technique that was beginning to make a lot of sense.

"An effective memory of the future has three components. First is a visual picture, the more tangible and detailed, the better. Are you familiar with the notion of cognitive dissonance?"

Charlie nodded, "It's when you try to hold two incompatible thoughts in your mind at the same time. Like a cigarette company executive insisting that he's a good person who doesn't want kids to smoke, and at the same time knowing he has to use advertising to entice children to become replacement smokers for the older customers being killed off."

"What happens?"

"Something has to give. Either he stops trying to hook kids, or he deceives himself into believing that, all evidence to the contrary, he really is a good guy who's not doing any harm."

"That's right," said Silvermane. "The same principle applies in creating memories of the future. If you have a vivid mental image of you as a successful entrepreneur living in a beautiful home, but the reality is that you're trapped in a job you hate, living in a crummy little apartment, something has to give. Either the picture decays into an idle daydream or vanishes altogether, or you figure out a way to start the business and move into the dream house."

"The second element is verbal affirmation, because while we dream in pictures, we tend to worry in words. You'll have a mental picture of this beautiful new house in your mind, and that nagging little voice of doubt will say, 'You can't afford the mortgage you have now! How are you gonna pay for that monstrosity?' That's when you need to remind yourself with affirmations that you are capable of achieving your goals."

Silvermane laughed as if some thought had reached out from the past and tickled his funny bone. "Remember the guy who made millions selling office volcanoes?"

Charlie wasn't sure whether or not to admit to having bought one. "You mean the little clay mountain with an indentation on top for lighting one of those charcoal snakes the kids always get on the Fourth of July?"

"That's the one." Silvermane was still laughing. "Hank Patton — he's the guy who thought up the idea — why, at first he could hardly give the things away. Then he came up with that magnificent advertising slogan — *Fire Up Your Office* — and the things started to fly off the shelves. It almost didn't happen, though. You see, Hank had a self-esteem problem. Every time he started making progress, he would do some foolish thing that would set him back financially, antagonize a key customer, one thing after another. He had a real fear of success, if you want to know the truth of it."

"I was on his board back then and tried to convince him to get some counseling, but he wouldn't hear of it. It was a macho thing. But one thing I did get him to do was change the way he talked to himself. He'd always been such a pessimist, expecting that the bank would call his loan, or that a big customer would back out of a deal. And of course, he seemed to have more than his share of those kind of problems."

"Well, one day after a board meeting I asked him if he talked to himself the same way he talked to us. 'What do you mean?' he asked, like I was implying he was crazy or something. But when I explained he said 'Heck NO! I give you guys the sugarcoated version. In my own mind I assume that everything will turn out worse than you could ever imagine. That way I can be ready for every possible disaster.'"

"No wonder we were having so many disasters! Old Hank was conjuring them up in this mind, and once something becomes clear enough in your mind, you can be sure you'll see it with your eyes before very long."

"What did you do?" Just that morning Charlie had been imagining a fight with LPI over his severance agreement, rejection by every company where he'd applied for a job, and having the bank cancel his personal line of credit now that he was starting to use it.

"It took some convincing, but I got Hank to change his inner scripts. Guess what? Within about three months, we stopped having a disaster every other week, and the company's sales started to take off. Now he's become such a believer that he puts everyone who comes into the company — from janitors to vice-presidents — through a course on visualization and self-talk. His company has been on the *Inc.* magazine list of the fastest growing companies for the past several years."

Charlie thought for a moment, then said, "I imagine it's most important to talk to yourself in a positive way at those times when it seems hardest to do — when you've been rejected at every turn and you're running out of money and feel like a failure." As he waited for Silvermane's response, he silently repeated one of the new affirmations he'd written for himself: "I am a winner, and I will turn every rejection into a future success. I will have the money I need at the time I need it, and when I am focused on my true mission, I will not be allowed to fail." It felt good to hear it up there inside his head, and he sat up a little straighter in his chair.

Charlie was writing again. "You said there were three components to a memory of the future. Mental visualization and verbal affirmations are the first two. What's the third?"

"Action!" Silvermane exclaimed. "Action. Without consistent, daily action that moves you in the direction of your goals, it's not a dream, it's a daydream." Silvermane let that sink in, then continued, "I've already talked about some of the tools that ambitious goals give you. I should also mention three incredible mental resources you have at your disposal, ready to be fired up as soon as you commit to your dream. I once had the privilege of meeting the late Napoleon Hill. He wrote one of the all-time classic self-help books, *Think and Grow Rich*. Have you read it?"

"A long time ago," Charlie muttered, not looking up from his steno pad.

"Well, read it again, and do it soon. Anyway, Mr. Hill told me that most people had it backwards. The average person believes he does-n't have time to think because he's too busy trying to make a living. Why, he was downright indignant about it. 'I didn't write a book called *Grow Rich and Think* for a reason,' he told me. 'If only people would use their minds.'"

Silvermane pointed to his head. "That's where the buried treasure is, Charlie. Right up here. You've got three precious resources that can help you attain any goal."

"The first is your attention. You know, people have no idea what a precious gift they are requesting when they ask someone for their attention. It's a much more valuable commodity even than time. The most important decisions you make have to do with what you pay attention to. Do you pay attention to bad news or good news? Do you pay attention to problems and scarcity or to opportunities and abundance?"

"I'd never really thought of it that way," Charlie said.

"Your attention account can't be overdrawn. Once you've given it away, it's gone. The second mental resource you have," Silvermane went on, once again indicating that Charlie should be writing this down, "is your imagination."

"It's such a precious gift but most people abuse it. They either squander it away conjuring up lurid images of a horrible future that they would never want to see — worry — or dreaming up beautiful pictures of an ideal existence that they have no intention whatsoever of trying to bring about — fantasy."

"Now, a little bit of worry and a little bit of daydreaming can be good things, but the most productive use of your imagination is creating memories of the future. It's the difference between Walt Disney building Cinderella's castle in the air and then laying a foundation under it, and the average Joe coming home at night, plopping down in front of the tube with a beer, and dreaming about winning the lottery so he'll never have to work again. Of course, when he's done fantasizing, he starts to worry again, because his problems are still there biting him on the ankles since he hasn't been thinking about how to solve them."

They had been speaking for over three hours now, and Silvermane showed no signs of fatigue. If anything, his energy and enthusiasm were growing as he went on.

"The other thing about imagination is that the more you work with it, the more you feed it information from many different areas, the more it will mature into intuition. And your intuition will lead you toward the people and actions you need in order to make that dream become real."

"Your third mental resource," he continued, "is belief. Belief is the essential catalyst that transforms a dream into a memory of the future. I called the first company I ever started the B-A-R corporation. Not very many people have asked me what the letters stood for, but they were an ongoing reminder to me — Believe, Achieve, Receive. That's something else most people have backwards. They want someone else to give them something — money, recognition, whatever — before they've earned it. Then they figure they'll go out and achieve something, because now they have the resources and the confidence to do it without taking too many uncomfortable risks. Then, only after they see everything starting to fall in place, will they really believe that this good thing is happening."

"You used the term 'fear of success' a while ago. I'd never really thought about it. I mean, why would anyone be afraid of something we all say we want more of?" Charlie asked.

"Good question. In my opinion, it's the biggest single obstacle facing anyone who sets his sites on building a business. First, most of us have a sneaking suspicion that we don't deserve success. We're taught from a very early age to not stand out, and that there's something wrong with having more than enough for yourself when there are people starving in India. You have to really believe that God wants you to be a rip-roaring success, and then be committed to sharing your success with other people."

"Second, people are more worried about what they might lose than what they could gain. They suspect that success brings a whole new set of obligations and they're going to become indentured to all the people who helped them climb the ladder."

"So how do you overcome the fear of success?" Charlie asked.

"You have to dream beyond the dream," Silvermane replied.

"Pardon me?"

"People today aren't willing to concentrate on one thing for an extended period of time to the exclusion of everything else. They want instant gratification."

Charlie laughed and said, "I'm sorry, but your comment just reminded me of a recent conversation I had with my fourteen-year-old daughter. I asked her if she understood the concept of delayed gratification. 'Well,' she replied, 'I think I know what delay means, and I certainly understand gratification, but when you put them together it's a...' and then she said, 'Dad, what's that word you like to use when two concepts don't go together? It sounds like a stupid cow?'"

"Oxymoron," Silvermane interjected, and both men laughed. "Yes, but it's not just your daughter's generation, it's also her parents' generation that thinks there's something slightly moronic about putting off small gratifications so they can someday have a big one. The paradox is that once they achieve that one big gratification that they've worked so hard for, all manner of other opportunities to do exciting and wonderful things that never before would have been possible come in its wake. If you want to be happy in the long run, it usually means denying yourself opportunities to have fun in the short run."

Silvermane stood up and walked over to the mantle above his fire-place. "I've won many awards in my day. Most of them are packed away in boxes somewhere, but I keep the important reminders up here." He picked up a picture frame.

"There are three documents in this frame, Charlie. One is the incorporation certificate for my first company, dated 1949. I had just finished college and set my mind on becoming a millionaire within two years."

"The second is a 1954 letter from a creditor threatening me with a lawsuit if I didn't pay an overdue bill that I had no way of paying at that time. So much for being a millionaire in two years!"

"The third is a hand-written note from my accountant, dated 1962. It says, 'Congratulations, Al! I've just completed your tax returns for the year and you are now officially a millionaire.' That's all. Want to know what I did when I got that note?"

"Celebrated?"

"Nope. I stuck it in my drawer and got back to work. I'd long since outgrown that goal. When it finally happened, it was no longer a goal, just a necessary waystation along the path to something bigger. Here's another paradox. Had I not outgrown that goal, I never would have achieved it. That's why you have to dream beyond the dream. As you grow, your old dreams get proportionately smaller. They stop inspiring you."

Silvermane replaced the picture frame. "I'll tell you why I didn't achieve that first goal of becoming a millionaire in record time. It was a false goal. Never frame your dreams, the ones that really count, in terms of money. Have a bigger dream than a pile of money and the money will be there as you need it. If all you dream of is having a pile of money, you never will, but you will have a heart full of worry."

"People think that all their problems would go away if a dumptruck would just come up and unload a small mountain of " money in their front yard. Actually, the only thing money does is give you the right to graduate to bigger and more interesting challenges than the problems you're facing right now."

"That's why you have to dream beyond the dream." As he said that, Silvermane invited Charlie to stand in a clear indication that the interview was over. "If there's an endpoint to your dream, like having a million dollars in the bank, even if it does happen, you won't keep it for very long. As soon as you stop striving toward the big goal far in front of you, you start slipping backwards."

As the two men shook hands, Charlie said, "Thanks, Mr. Silvermane, you've given me a lot to think about."

Silvermane smiled. "Charlie, it's too early for you to start thinking. You'll just think your way back into the same old box. Now is the time for you to be dreaming! Mountain-sized dreams! Thinking is the tool by which you chisel those mountains down into magnificent works of art. But first, you must find the right mountains.

Three paradoxes occur when you set your sights on a big goal:

1. What you stand to gain is far larger than what you can lose, and the downside risk is usually the same no matter what the upside potential

2. Audicious goals are more likely to be achieved than timid ones

3. Audicious goals bcome the platform for bigger and better dreams.

Why ambitious goals are more likely to succeed than timid ones:

1. When you're committed to a big goal it's a magnet that attracts the people and money that you need

2. When you've got your bearings fixed on a big mountain, you're less likely to be drawn down side paths

3. When you have a huge goal you learn to focus your time and energy

4. A big dream keeps you going on bad days

Elements of a Memory of the Future:

1. Mental visualization

2. Verbal affirmations

3. Action

Mental Resources:

1. Attention

2. Imagination

3. Belief

4

Stop Worrying
So You Can Start Winning

"You look worried again, Charlie. What is it this time?"

Mitch Matsui had been one of Charlie's best friends since their days at St. Johns. He was the class philosopher, and over the years Charlie had always consulted with him on important decisions. It had been Mitch's idea to go hiking in the Grand Canyon. Charlie was struggling with whether to follow his dreams and go into business for himself or to give in to his fears and doubts and get a "real job." Mitch suggested that a week in the desert would help him focus on his priorities.

It took Charlie a moment to reorient himself from the inner world, in which he'd been mentally wandering, back to the outer world through which he was now walking. Emerging from the deep pit of his anxieties into the magnificent cathedral of the Grand Canyon took Charlie's breath away.

"Did you see the bighorn sheep looking down at us from the butte back half a mile or so," asked Mitch. "Or that pair of hawks circling the pinnacle across the river?"

Mitch had passed up many lucrative opportunities in the business world to stay on and teach at the college. If his classmates had ever felt sorry for Mitch struggling to get by on a teacher's salary, they didn't anymore. His first book of poetry, *Live Your Dreams Before They Come True*, was an international bestseller, as were the sequels, and he now had more invitations for speaking engagements than he could possibly accept. Through all his success, Mitch remained the humble philosopher. He didn't even take credit for the book. "I was just lucky enough to be the official translator for the poetry of McZen," he'd say, though no one really believed that McZen was anything other than a figment of Mitch's imagination.

"Well?" Mitch dragged Charlie from his inner thoughts. "What are you worrying about this time? What mental weight is so heavy that it's keeping you from appreciating..." and here Mitch simply spread his arms as if to capture the grandeur.

"Oh, nothing," Charlie replied. "I was just thinking about how my being unemployed has affected my family."

Mitch took several steps off the trail and picked up a chunk of granite that Charlie guessed weighed nearly a pound. "This seems to be about the right size for that worry."

Mitch walked over to Charlie and unzipped the lower compartment of his backpack. "Oh man," Charlie groaned, "I don't need to carry another rock!"

"You certainly don't," Mitch agreed, "which makes me wonder why you go out of your way to pick them up."

At the start of their trek, Charlie had agreed to go along with one of Mitch's wild ideas. Every time he caught Charlie worrying, Mitch would pick up a stone and put it into his friend's backpack. Carrying those rocks around would be a metaphor for the emotional weight of all of the worries with which Charlie had burdened himself. Now, Charlie regretted the decision. His shoulders ached under the burden of more than twenty rocks. While Mitch bounded across the trail as though his backpack was filled with helium balloons, Charlie felt like one of the pack mules they'd seen laboring down the trail.

"Let's go, my friend," Mitch said. "A few more hours and we'll stop for lunch. Then we'll have a cairn ceremony."

"A what?"

"It's time to take some of the weight off your shoulders," Mitch replied. "I'll explain how it works at lunch."

Mitch speeded on ahead, telling Charlie he had to make preparations for the ceremony. Before they parted, he made Charlie promise that any time he caught himself worrying he himself would add another rock to his pack. For the next three hours Charlie kept his eyes on the scenery about him and his mind off his cares.

At last, Charlie saw where Mitch had set up for lunch. He dropped his heavy pack, retrieved his water bottle, doused his face and then his thirst. During lunch, neither man said much. Afterward, Mitch asked Charlie to lay his rock collection out on the ground. "Look at all these worries," Mitch exclaimed. "No wonder you always feel so weighed down!"

"It's a lot easier to carry around the ones you can't see," Charlie replied.

"Is it really? It seems to me that they take a greater toll, and can be harder to leave behind."

As he looked at the pile of rocks, Charlie wished that it was as easy to empty his mind of worries as it had been to empty his backpack of rocks.

"How do you define worry?" Mitch asked.

"I guess it's thinking about bad things that might happen in the future," Charlie replied.

Mitch smiled. "That's probably what 99 out of 100 people would say, and it's OK as far as it goes. But, if you want to beat the worry habit the first step is to understand what worry really is."

"Actually, I have many definitions for worry. Like this one: Worry is a money repellent."

"What do you mean, it's a money repellent?" Charlie asked.

"If there's something you really want to get done, you'll find the money. Somehow, money arrives in just the right increments at just the right time. But, as soon as you start worrying about how you're going to pay for the project, you've taken the first step to killing it."

"That's ridiculous," retorted Charlie. "How can worrying about money drive money away?"

"When you worry about money, you're seeing the world as a place of scarcity. When you trust that the money will come when you need it, you're seeing the world as a place of abundance. In our entrepreneur's club we read the book *Think and Grow Rich* by Napoleon Hill. Well, he didn't call it *Worry and Grow Rich*. You're more likely to worry yourself into the poor house than you are to worry yourself into a mansion."

Charlie shook his head. "Then why do so many wealthy people worry so much about money?"

Mitch picked up a rock. "To have a great deal of money does not make one wealthy. McZen said that broke is a state of wallet; poverty is a state of mind."

Mitch held a hand out toward Charlie's rocks. "Many of these rocks that you've been carrying around for the past four days are about money. Has all that worrying made you any wealthier?"

Charlie looked at the rocks. "No, of course not. But every time I think about starting my own business, I worry that I don't have enough of a cushion."

Mitch smiled. "What's the worst thing that can happen if you start a business and it fails? Will you be put in debtors' prison, or made to work as a galley slave to pay your debts off?"

"Of course not," Charlie snorted. "Those things haven't been done for centuries."

"So what *is* the absolute worst thing that can happen?" Mitch persisted.

"Well," Charlie replied, "I'm sure declaring bankruptcy is no walk in the park!" Charlie picked up one of his rocks and added it to the cairn.

"It's not the end of the world either. Pick up any issue of *Success* or *Entrepreneur* magazine and you'll read about somebody who has overcome bankruptcy and gone on to great success and wealth."

"I know, Mitch, but after so many years of having a regular paycheck..."

Mitch laughed softly. "Here's something else McZen said: Someone with a job is never secure; someone with a calling is never unemployed." Charlie remembered Cheryl having quoted that line.

Now Mitch became serious. "The only employment security in the world today is loving your work, and doing it with confidence and enthusiasm."

Mitch placed another one of Charlie's stones on the pile. "A cairn is a pile of rocks that a traveler builds to show the way for those who come behind. If you keep your eyes open, Charlie, you'll find that the world is full of cairns. And that's what we're doing on this trip. We're building a set of guideposts. For example, here's a guidepost to help you stop worrying about money problems. No matter how much you get paid, as long as you're working on a per hour basis you've only got a job or—how does Cheryl put it?—J-O-B: Jilted, Obsolete, and Broke."

Charlie leaned back, savoring the warmth of the midday sun. "You know what would be the worst thing about bankruptcy? It would be the humiliation of it all. The way old friends would avoid you, and the way all those people who told you to get a real job would be gloating. I could just imagine people telling their children to work harder in school so they don't end up like poor old Charlie McKeever!"

Mitch added another rock to the cairn. "You know, Charlie, you'd worry a lot less about what other people think of you if you knew how infrequently they think of you. Your ego wants you to believe that you are the center of the universe, which is laughable when you look at the magnificent sculptures in this canyon."

"It's funny, Mitch, but just about everyone I've talked to in the past month has come back to ego as if it were a big wall standing between you and your dreams."

Mitch leaned forward and rummaged through the remaining rocks, finally picking up an ugly brown one, the biggest of the lot, and placed it atop the cairn. "Worry is the natural state of ego."

"When you worry about something, it makes you feel important-like if something bad happens to you the universe will somehow be a diminished place. It's a lot easier to worry about a problem than it is to do the work required to fix it. Have you ever noticed how it always seems like there's something more urgent you should be doing?"

Charlie smiled. "With the exception of this very moment, that's been pretty much a chronic situation in my life."

"Put another rock on the cairn, Charlie. Ego gains a sense of importance by having so many seemingly urgent things to do. By worrying about them all it never has to get around to actually doing them."

"You talk about ego as if it's some sort of alien body. But it's an essential part of who I am, isn't it? And isn't it good to have a strong ego?"

"Of course," replied Mitch. "Ego is just a word to describe a deeper reality. And that reality is often one of inner conflict — as when you try to decide between doing what you think you want to do and what you think other people expect. Boiled down to its essence, it's the age-old conflict between ego and soul."

"They are always in conflict, ego and soul. When you're worried and agitated, you know that ego is in control. When you are at peace and feeling a sense of faith, you know that soul is in control." Mitch had picked up a rock and was tossing it back and forth between his two hands as he spoke.

"Ego seeks security, soul seeks adventure. Ego is a hanging on, soul is a letting go. Ego is anxiety, soul is faith."

Mitch scooped up the remaining rocks from Charlie's backpack and stacked them up on the cairn. "Here's another definition: Worry is an abuse of your imagination. Instead of using your imagination to dream a beautiful future, you use it to manufacture nightmares. When you're full of anxiety, two bad things happen to shut down imagination and intuitive intelligence. First, your perceptions of reality are distorted, as if you are looking at the world, and yourself, through a funhouse mirror. When you're full of anxiety, problems always seem bigger than they really are, and your own resources and strengths seem a lot smaller."

"The other thing that happens is that you simply do not see options that would be available to you if you were full of faith and confidence. There is always something to worry about. The challenge is to replace *worrying* about problems with *thinking* about solutions."

Mitch brushed the dust from his hands. "That's quite a respectable pile we've built, isn't it? When we start walking again, we'll leave all these rocks behind. Maybe they'll help someone else find the path. And maybe, you can leave your worries behind. You move a lot faster when you travel light!"

"I wish it was that simple," Charlie replied.

"It *is* that simple." Mitch leaned in Charlie's direction. "How long have you been down here in the Grand Canyon?"

"Same as you, Mitch. About four days."

"No, Charlie, up until now your mind has been somewhere else. When you keep your attention anchored in the present, you can start to break the worry habit. That's the secret to overcoming worry Charlie: keep your mind and your body in the same time zone. Almost all emotional pain is caused by time travel — either guilt, regret and anger from the past, or fear and anxiety about the future. When you keep your attention anchored in the present, you can start to break the worry habit."

"The images you run through your mind today will profoundly influence the outcomes you get in the future. If you spend a lot of time worrying that your kid will turn into a juvenile delinquent, the worry itself can cause you to act in ways that acutally bring it about. On the other hand, if you have faith that your children will turn out fine, even as they go through adolescent rough spots, chances are that's what will end up happening."

The two men packed their gear and resumed their trek, leaving behind the cairn piled with worry stones. At length, Mitch spoke, "I said that breaking the worry habit was simple, but not easy. We've covered the simple part — to keep your attention in the present and stop being so concerned about pleasing and impressing other people. If you'd like, I can share with you some of the practical action steps that have helped me break out of the worry habit."

"I'd like that a lot," Charlie replied.

"As I said, it's simple but not easy. You have to discipline yourself. The first step is to take care of your physical body. Descartes was wrong when he said that mind and body are totally separate. What happens in one influences the performance of the other. Besides being tired and sore, how have you felt the past few days — I mean emotionally?"

Charlie stretched his shoulders back. "Great!"

"Part of the reason," said Mitch, "is that you're taking care of your body's four essential needs. First is simply to get enough sleep. When you deprive yourself of adequate sleep, you're much more likely to suffer from worry, anxiety and depression. Out here on the trail, there's nothing to do after the sun goes down. So we talk for a while, then go to sleep, at an hour probably much earlier than you're used to."

"And you know what? I haven't missed those late night TV shows — not even the news."

"The second thing you've been doing," Mitch went on, "is getting proper nutrition. You scowled at me when I gave you a baggie full of vitamins and mineral pills for each day of the trip, but taking them has given you greater physical energy, which builds your emotional fortitude."

"And you know what?" Charlie asked. "Taking those tablets really isn't so bad, once you get used to it."

"Especially if you take them with water," Mitch laughed. "Ironically, I'll bet that out here in the desert you're better hydrated than you are back at home. That's because we're not filling up on caffeinated drinks that dehydrate you even as they seem to quench your thirst. So the third thing to keep doing when you get back is drinking plenty of water during the day. The fourth thing you're doing, quite obviously, is getting exercise — probably a lot more than you're used to getting."

"Now there's an understatement," laughed Charlie, "although I feel a lot better now that I'm not carrying half the canyon in my pack!"

"If you read all the books on how to overcome depression and anxiety," Mitch continued, "one of the common themes will be to get physical exercise. This is important for two reasons. First, the exercise itself is a safe release for the stress that can create physical and emotional problems. Second, when your body is strong, you're better able to cope with the daily demands that can seem so stressful."

They walked on in silence until Mitch stopped and pulled the topographical map out of his pack. "I'm about to demonstrate something else that's important to controlling your worry. It's advice from the great German poet Rilke: doubt can be paralyzing, but you can train it by forcing it to ask good questions. For example, right now I'm looking at what appears to be a trail that will take us south, back up to the top of the rim. Is it Grandview Trail? If it is, then we need to turn here. If it's not, and we turn here anyway thinking that it is, we could end up in a lot of trouble. So what do we do?"

"Mitch, you're the guide. Please don't tell me you're lost!"

"McZen says that if you don't have a question, you don't have a clue; if you're not searching, you must be lost."

"Listen, Mitch, right now I couldn't care less what McZen says. Are we lost?"

"Charlie, your doubt is pushing you toward a panic attack. When you panic, you make bad decisions. Train your doubt, and start right now. First, how much water do we have — how long will it last us in a worst case?"

"We just filled the camelback," Charlie replied, "so we could probably go for several days if we're careful."

"Excellent! Instead of creating visions of two desiccated skeletons on the trail, your doubt now knows that we have enough water to make it back to Cremation Creek if we need to, and in a worst case we could refill our water containers there and hike back to the trail we came down in the first place. Take a look at the topo map and tell me if you can approximate where we are. Since you know where we started this morning."

Charlie scrutinized the map and made an educated guess as to their current location. "Not bad," Mitch responded. "This is the trailhead that we need to get up on Horseshoe Mesa, which is our stop for tonight. Look around and tell me if you see this shape."

Charlie pointed to a large structure off to the right. "Very good, Charlie, that's terrific!"

"You mean I got it right?"

"No, actually you didn't. But you did point to something that looks a bit like Horseshoe Mesa. Look closer, though. It's not high enough. You see how Horseshoe Mesa towers above the surrounding terrain on the map here, but what you just pointed to is actually lower than the surrounding structures? How about that?" he continued, pointing to a plateau that was much more distant than what Charlie was looking at.

Charlie shook his head. "Now I'm really confused," he said. "That's good," Mitch replied. "Now you can start to learn. You see, two minutes ago you were panicked. One minute ago you thought you knew the answer. Now you're willing to ask questions. You're learning to train your doubt." Mitch showed Charlie how to read the map correctly, and to feel confident enough to locate the trail that would lead them out of the canyon. If nothing else, Charlie thought, this trip would give him a whole new appreciation for poets.

"There are three more things that can help you deal more effectively with worry," Mitch said. "The first is to follow the old advice to prepare for the worst, but expect the best. That's really what we've done on this journey. We are carrying all sorts of first aid supplies that we don't expect to use, but which could be life-saving."

"The second is to reprogram your negative and pessimistic thinking patterns. When we get back, I'd like to give you the name of a woman who does hyper-hypnosis. It's an incredibly intense experience that can help you eradicate negative thought patterns and get out of emotional ruts."

"And the last thing is from another of McZen's poems. It says when you're afraid of the future you should concentrate on what you must do right now today, and when you're afraid of what's happening today, you should keep your vision on the future. How can you do them both at once? I don't know what the answer is for you, but I do know that to be both happy and successful, that's exactly what you must do."

That night, their last in the canyon, the two men lay under the stars. Charlie had always believed that whenever he saw a shooting star, it portended good things. That night, the sky seemed to be alive with them.

TO OVERCOME WORRY:

1. Anchor your attention in the present

2. Don't be concerned about pleasing and impressing people

3. Take care of your body's four essential needs - sleep, nutrition, hydration, exercise

4. Train your doubt

5. Prepare for the worst, but expect the best

6. Reprogram negative thinking patterns

7. Keep your attention in the present and your vision in the future

5

CLEAN UP THE MESS IN YOUR ATTIC

WHEN MITCH MATSUI RECOMMENDED HYPER-HYPNOSIS, CHARLIE HAD imagined an old woman in long purple robes with gold hoop earrings. However, his introduction to Ronda Wellington had been quite different.

Wellington had sent him a pre-appointment survey which took the better part of a day to complete. It asked him to catalog all of his fears and guilt feelings, his worries, sources of stress, causes of procrastination, and self-sabotaging attitudes. If he had ever had a negative thought, Wellington's questionnaire wanted to know about it.

Her brochure had explained hyper-hypnosis as a full day of hypnotherapy, a sort of all-out assault on self-imposed limitations. "This is a massive intervention that is designed to interrupt self-defeating attitudes and behavior patterns, and through metaphorical visualization to replace them with more useful mental tools."

Now, walking into Wellington's office, Charlie saw what could have been the waiting room in any business. There were no crystal balls, no magic charms, and no parrot squawking omens of dread and doom.

Charlie checked in and the receptionist escorted him to a room at the back of the office suite. On the door was a sign that read:

QUIET PLEASE
MIRACLES WITHIN

Inside was a room much more like what Charlie had expected in the first place. It had thick carpeting, and was lighted only by a shaded lamp. There was no desk, only a wooden captain's chair, and against one wall the most comfortable-looking black leather lounge chair Charlie had ever seen. The soft music of flutes and guitar suffused the room.

"Dr. Wellington will be with you in a moment. Why don't you make yourself comfortable," the receptionist said, motioning toward the easy chair. His pre-appointment instructions had told Charlie to get a good night of sleep so he wouldn't fall asleep during the session, but it was still a struggle to stay alert as he waited.

He'd almost fallen asleep when the door opened and a woman who appeared to be in her mid-fifties walked in. She was wearing a sharp blue business suit — no flowing purple robes! "Good morning, Charlie. I've spent so much time with your survey that I feel like I know you."

Charlie felt like a turtle on its back as he struggled to work his way out of the easy chair, but she motioned him to stay seated. "I'm Dr. Wellington, Ronda Wellington." She shook Charlie's hand, then took her place in the captain's chair.

"You've read the brochure, so you know this will be a very intense day." She placed a clipboard on her lap. "Metaphorical visualization is a revolutionary method for rewriting some of the harmful scripts, negative self images, and destructive attitudes that can hold you back." Her manner exuded caring and competence, and Charlie felt a bond of trust.

"Basically, it's psychological judo. Rather than tackle the problems head on, we'll create visual and verbal metaphors — pictures of something else to represent the problems you would like to solve, and the tools you will need to solve them. Here's an example." She looked from Charlie down to her clipboard.

"You enjoy automobile racing, don't you?"

Charlie nodded.

"Imagine you have a busy day before you: projects to complete, meetings to attend, places to go, family and social activities, and so on. Instead of getting up in the morning and making a to-do list, you visualize your day as a Formula One racecourse. The projects that you are not looking forward to appear as tricky hairpin curves, and the fun stuff as long straightaways. Once you have the course all mapped out, you picture yourself, all fueled up and ready to go. Whenever you get bogged down during the day, you recall the vision of yourself powering through the curves. That's metaphorical visualization."

"Sounds like fun," said Charlie.

"It is," replied Dr. Wellington. "In fact, it all started more than ten years ago when I was working with children to help them raise their self-esteem. Our most effective results came from these little mind games. Since then, we've adapted the technique to a whole range of conditions."

"Like helping people get unstuck?" Charlie asked.

"That's ninety percent of my business," responded Dr. Wellington. "Think of your mind as the attic in the house of your body. Like most attics everywhere, over time it becomes filled with all sorts of stuff — some of it useful, much of it not. And that's what *The Janitor In Your Attic* is all about."

"The janitor in my attic? Sounds kind of silly."

"Have any of the more serious things you've tried been very effective?"

"Not really," Charlie replied, "and certainly not as much fun."

"You know what? Having fun turns out to be one of the most important predictors of success. The two others are faith and repetition. Now, I can't make any guarantees, but I will tell you that the more confident you are that this will help you, the more likely it is to help."

"The more certain you are that it will work, and the more you practice it, the better you'll get, and the better your outcomes will be. I'm going to give you some tapes to take home and listen to every day for the next several months."

"Close your eyes for a minute now; visualize your own attic — your mind. Think of all the memories, the emotions, the thoughts, the facts and figures, the fears and doubts, the desires and ambitions, all that stuff that's up there fighting for your attention. Describe your attic for me, Charlie."

"Chaos. It's a mess."

"Some of the things that have been hardwired into your mind — like the fight-or-flight reflex — are obsolete. For most of the problems we face today, fighting or running away is counterproductive."

Charlie thought about his final meeting with Dick Dierdron. He'd wanted to punch him in the nose and then run and hide. "I know what you mean," he smiled sheepishly.

"We're going to structure our day into four segments. First we'll go up into 'your attic' and clean up the mess. In session two, we'll give you tools that will help you master your emotions.

In session three, we'll go through a routine that you should repeat every morning to help program yourself for a great day. And finally, I'll give you an evening routine that will help you wind down and prepare for the following day."

Charlie leaned back. "Okay, I'm ready," he exclaimed.

"Before we get started, I need to introduce you to two important characters who are up there in your attic. The first character is nasty. He's a gremlin, a vandal. He's the one who is responsible for all of the negative self-talk, the sudden fears and worries, the self-imposed limitations, and all the other mental garbage that keeps you stuck in your rut. Can you picture him running around up there, Charlie? Can you picture him painting graffiti on the walls of your mind? Things like,

'Get a real job,' and 'You don't have what it takes to make it in the big time?'"

Charlie could see the picture clearly.

"What's his name, Charlie?"

Without even thinking Charlie said, "Gollum!"

"From Tolkien's *Hobbit* Classics. How appropriate," Dr. Wellington replied. "Now, Charlie, imagine that you have a janitor up there, whose job it is to run around and clean up after Gollum. Someone who can help you clean up the mess and give you the tools to start building your attic into the nice place that you want it to be. Can you picture him?"

Charlie sat quietly for a while, then smiled and nodded his head. "What's his name?" Dr. Wellington asked.

"Spike! Spike was my high school football coach. He could handle any gremlin!"

"Very good, Charlie. Very good."

"Now, Charlie, let's go up into the attic and straighten things out. Visualize yourself crawling up into the attic. When you get there, visualize the mess, the chaos. All that mess is the work of Gollum. You don't see Gollum right now, Charlie, because like most gremlins of his ilk, Gollum is a coward. As soon as you shine a light on him, he runs away."

"Now, visualize Spike coming in to help clean up the mess. The first thing he's going to do is clean out all the garbage. There's a ton of garbage, isn't there, Charlie? For a lifetime, your mind has been letting all kinds of garbage in. Oh, you weren't conscious of it at the time, but you let it in and it stayed."

"Let's start with the easy stuff," she continued. "Almost every time you've watched television or gone to a movie, you've absorbed images of violence and negativity. Although you haven't been consciously aware of it, these images have slowly and insidiously shaped for you a vision of the world as a frightening and hostile place. Now, relax and breathe slowly; picture in your mind a garbage dumpster that's open at the top. Visualize Spike walking around with a broom and a dustbin, sweeping up all the images of hatred, violence, rejection, and death that you've seen during the thousands of hours you've spent in front of the television. Watch him dump those images right back into the garbage dumpster. Can you see him, Charlie, sweeping the place up?" Charlied nodded again.

"Concentrate, Charlie, fix that picture in your mind. Keep watching Spike, sweeping out those frightening and negative images." Charlie's brow furrowed as he struggled to keep the picture in his mind. Dr. Wellington continued, "Now, picture Spike driving up in a big forklift and hoisting that garbage dumpster full of negative images. Can you see it?" Charlie nodded "Watch him drive the forklift over to a great big dump truck, raise the lift as high as it will go, and drop all those negative images into a dump truck. Can you see it, Charlie? Imagine that on the side of the truck the words are painted, 'Garbage Out.'"

"Oh, Charlie, there's so much work to be done up here! Spike's just getting warmed up. Can you see him rolling up his sleeves like he really means business?" Charlie responded by simple squeezing his eyes more tightly shut as he struggled to keep the image in his mind. The music had become deeper and darker, with bassoons and bass replacing the flutes and guitar.

"Your attic is also full of mirrors — funhouse mirrors. They are what creates your image of yourself, and they're often not very flattering. That's because most of the mirrors in *your* attict are funhouse mirrors! What you see when you look in them is not the real Charlie, but a twisted and distorted caricature. Those mirrors have to go! Can you see yourself walking up to one of those mirrors? That's the mirror Gollum put up to create a distorted reflection of your business self."

"And here comes Spike, pulling a hammer out of his belt. Watch him, Charlie, as he rips it off the wall. It's heavy, so he struggles to carry it to the dumpster. Watch him hoist it over the side, then listen to the shattering glass as it hits the bottom. Picture Spike hanging another mirror in its place, a normal mirror. See the real Charlie McKeever, capable and trustworthy."

"Now watch Spike push his cart along to the next mirror. This is Charlie the parent. It's not the parent your children see—at least not most of the time, but it's the picture Gollum wants you to see: spoiling your children rotten, doing a lousy job of disciplining, always at work when you should be at home—is this a familiar reflection Charlie?" Charlie nodded.

"Familiar, but not real. The real image is you struggling to do your best to meet what often feels like an impossible load of demands. The things you are doing right outweigh the ones you're not doing right. So let's have Spike rip down this mirror and dump it—can you hear the glass shatter at the bottom of the dumpster?—and put up a new mirror, one that reflects the real Charlie McKeever, who is a loving and devoted husband and father."

Charlie's lip quivered as he thought about his family, and how badly he wanted to do the right thing for them.

"There are many more mirrors to be removed, Charlie. That will be one of your assignments in the coming months. But if you look closely, you'll notice something else on the walls of your attic up there—lots of graffiti. That's the negative self talk, the doubt, the false beliefs that hold you back. You see, Charlie, Gollum is basically a lazy coward. He doesn't want to work hard, and he's afraid of change. So he paints the walls with lies about you and your abilities. You see those lies every day, and you begin to believe them."

Charlie felt as though a black cloud of dread had moved in and settled over him. Dr. Wellington's pre-appointment survey had asked him to list all his negative self-talk and his list had gone on for three pages. Now the entire list was playing back though his head.

"Gollum is painting on the walls up there again, isn't he?" Dr. Wellington asked. Charlie nodded. "That's a good sign. He's feeling threatened. And here comes Spike, just in time."

Charlie clamped his eyes shut. "Spike is pushing a cart full of paint cans and brushes. Pay attention, Charlie. He's prying the lid off of a can of paint. Now watch him go up to each piece of graffiti, all those lies that Gollum keeps repeating in your head, and cover them up with clean white paint. And from the bottom of his cart, Spike pulls out a beautiful needlepoint sign and hangs it on the wall where the graffiti was. Can you read it, Charlie? It says, 'I Am a Winner and Winners Don't Quit.'

"You made the most important step before you ever came to my office, Charlie, and that was when you wrote down your list of negative self talk. Now you can recognize it for what it is, and every time it comes up, holler for Spike to paint it out, and replace it with something that's positive."

"In the pre-appointment survey, Charlie, you described your dream of the ideal future. It's a beautiful dream: building a business that creates jobs and touches many lives in a positive way; spending your days doing work that you love to do; building your dream house out in the country."

"I want you to picture that dream now Charlie, see your ideal future as a beautiful garden. On the canvas of your mind, paint a place that is alive with flowers, plants and trees. Let each tree, every flower, represent a goal that you have accomplished. Walk through your garden. That's the future you deserve Charlie. A place of splendor and peace."

Dr. Wellington sat quietly for several minutes, allowing Charlie to savor the image. Then she continued, "That picture, that garden, is your certainty. It's your destiny — your memory of the future. But you can't always see it so clearly, can you? It's as if some days your garden has been choked over by weeds. Those weeds are your doubts about yourself, about your ideas, about other people, doubts about money — your doubts are the weeds choking the garden. While you're out there in the future building your beautiful garden — your memory of the future — your little gremlin, Gollum, is up in the attic planting seeds of doubt. Unless you take immediate action they can choke out the flowers before they have a chance to grow."

As Charlie visualized the garden of his dream future being choked over by weeds, he felt an infinite sadness, an emptiness he had not experienced since his beloved boyhood dog was hit by a car. He felt helpless and paralyzed as he watched a jungle of weeds sprouting, creeping, and blossoming throughout his garden. Then, as each one opened its hideous head to the sun, it spewed out a horde of new doubts.

"I want you to picture yourself looking into your garden. You can only catch glimpses through the forest of weeds. Can you see that Charlie?"

Charlie nodded. "You feel helpless, don't you? Helpless and furious." Charlie felt again the emptiness he'd experienced at the funeral of his dog.

"Now, Charlie, focus in on the image of you. Notice that you're wearing work clothes — denim coveralls and heavy work boots. Can you see that?" Charlie nodded. "Notice that you're wearing industrial eyeglasses and ear protection. Can you see it?" Charlie nodded again.

"Take a closer look at your face, Charlie. Have you ever seen such a look of determination? You are the hero, Charlie, who will not give up the quest without a gallant fight." Dr. Wellington noticed Charlie's jaw set.

"You are the hero, but there's one thing missing. You need a weapon, don't you? Look down at your hands, Charlie, and take a look at what you're holding. It is a giant..." she paused as Charlie's fingers clenched to grasp his imaginary weapon.

"...Weedwhacker!" A smile lit up Charlie's face. "Watch yourself pull the starter, and hear it roar into action. What you have in your hands is Sears' best-quality industrial-strength weedwhacker. And you're a hero on a mission. Your mission, Charlie, is to save the garden of your future dreams from those weeds of doubt. Rev up your weedwhacker, Charlie."

By now, Charlie was totally absorbed. At length Dr. Wellington spoke again: "Oh, good, here comes Spike. He's pushing a great big wheelbarrow and has a couple of rakes. It's time to set aside the weedwhacker and get rid of the carnage. Do you see yourself and Spike raking up all those dead weeds and throwing them in the wheelbarrow?" Charlie nodded. "Good. Once the wheelbarrow is full, Spike will take them out to be burned. And while he does that, you will spread weed killer all around the garden. But I must warn you, weeds of doubt are not like ordinary weeds. They are resilient. This garden is like any other, though. If you will spend a little time weeding it every day, it will stay beautiful."

"Now, picture yourself again. There's dirt all over your face, except where your safety glasses were. Your clothes are filthy, and your boots caked with mud. But there's a great big smile on your face." Charlie smiled. "Now, just walk around your garden for a bit. Imagine all the people you work with, the people you give jobs to, the people you help, all wandering around admiring the garden. And off in the distance, up on a small hill, your dream house faces out over the pond. You've worked hard, and you've earned it."

Dr. Wellington was quiet for a long time, allowing Charlie to revel in the dream. "There's one more job we have to do, Charlie, and I've saved the most difficult, and most dangerous job for last. When you were preparing yourself for this visit, I had you make a list of the fears you see holding yourself back. It was quite a list Charlie, an ugly list. Gollum has taken all of your fears — failure, rejection, bankruptcy, humiliation, commitment, and cemented them together into a massive stone of dread. Visualize this boulder now, Charlie — the jagged edges that cause you so much pain. It's too big to move, because by the time Gollum has added all of your fears, it's not just a boulder — it's a small mountain. What are we going to do with this huge rock of fear, Charlie?"

Charlie shook his head and shrugged.

"We're going to blow it up, Charlie, blast it to smithereens! For this job, Spike needs professional help. Picture a road leading up to that big rock of fear. You and Spike are standing at the end of the road, in the shadow of the rock, and you're waiting."

This was Dr. Wellington's favorite part. It was why she called metaphorical visualization her "magical science." At some point during every successful session, the process became something magic. That was happening now. She and Charlie were synchronizing. She felt herself being guided to the images that would be most effective in helping Charlie get unstuck.

"You and Spike are looking at this hideous boulder, wondering how you can ever get it out of the way, when you hear a rumbling noise headed in your direction. You see a column of dust rising in the distance. Now you see it's a convoy of trucks. Spike tells you it's the demolition team he's called for. They're going to blow up the rock, and haul out the pieces."

Dr. Wellington paused to allow Charlie to paint the mental image. "The convoy pulls to a stop. A couple of Humvees at the front, and then a whole line of bulldozers and dump trucks. A man jumps out of the leading vehicle."

"He's Spike's friend Ramrock, the demolition expert. Now you see men pile out and begin drilling holes and then stuffing them full of explosives."

"Watch Ramrock going around and carefully inspecting each charge. Now they've lined up all the dump trucks to form a protective shield, and you and Spike are huddled down behind a great big wheel. You hear Ramrock hollering for everyone to get down, and look up just in time to see him pushing the plunger of the detonator. There is a searing flash of light and heat, followed by the loudest explosion you've ever heard. Then the rocks start falling."

"When the dust finally clears, you crawl out from under the truck and watch Ramrock's team go to work. There are bulldozers everywhere. When all the rocks have been cleaned up, Ramrock says goodbye and you and Spike turn around. There in the distance is your dream, your memory of the future, and the rock of fear no longer stands in your way."

"It's a beautiful day and you are experiencing a freedom you've not felt in a long time—freedom from fear. Your attic is clean. We've taken all of the garbage out—the mirrors, the graffiti, the weeds of doubt, the rocks of fear, it's all gone. I'm going to leave for a while now Charlie, and let you enjoy your freedom. When I come back, we'll begin our second session, where we give you the tools to achieve your memory of the future."

Charlie was still resting in the chair when Dr. Wellington returned and asked how he was doing.

"I think I have a headache from when Ramrock demolished that rock."

They both laughed, then sat in silence for a moment before Dr. Wellington asked Charlie if he was ready to continue. He nodded. "See yourself pulling down the ladder again and climbing up into the attic of your mind. Take a look around and enjoy it, Charlie, because you might not ever see your attic this clean again."

"For this next session," Dr. Wellington continued, "we're going to be doing some heavy construction. Working in your attic is a lot like refurbishing an old house—it's a project that never ends. But in this session, we're going to install the equipment and machinery that will help you keep Gollum under control, and stay focused on your memories of the future."

"The first step is to give you a way to keep your attic organized. Every day, you are faced with a barrage of new information, old memories, thoughts and emotions, and it can be overwhelming at times. So we're going to visualize Spike constructing a massive set of shelving in the warehouse section of the attic. Imagine Spike putting up steel shelves, row after row of them."

"Now, Charlie, imagine Spike carrying in boxes of all different sizes, shapes, and colors and putting them neatly on the shelves. He's putting some on the shelves labeled 'Emotions,' or 'Names to Remember,' others are labeled 'Facts' and 'Figures.' As he goes, he's sorting out the knowledge, emotions and thoughts, everything that goes on in your head."

"Here's how you're going to use those shelves, you and Spike. Every time you learn something new, you'll take a second to visualize Spike putting that box of information in the proper place on the shelves. Likewise, every time you meet a new person, you'll close your eyes for just a second to visualize Spike putting a box with that person's name and image in the right place on the shelves. Any time you have a hard time remembering something or someone, rather than fighting to dig up the name, you will simply visualize Spike going back through the shelves and bringing you the right box. Over time, you will learn to trust Spike, and your intuition."

"Okay, take one last look back at the warehouse. Are all the boxes up off the floor and on the shelves?" Charlie nodded. *If only it would be so easy* he heard a small voice inside his head say. And then another voice replied, *It can be.*

"The next thing Spike needs to do is install fire alarm and sprinkler systems. Often, your emotions act the same way a fire does. They build up slowly, creating stress and tension. Then, seemingly without warning, they erupt into a full-blown temper tantrum, panic attack, or stress-out. The trick is to see it coming and then have a system to douse the flames before they rage out of control and cause you to do something or say something you'll later regret. So picture Spike putting up smoke detectors throughout the attic. They will be your early warning system for the fires of anger, stress, and fear."

"Here comes Spike again, and this time he's pushing a cart loaded with PVC piping for your emotional fire sprinkler system. As you watch Spike installing the sprinkler heads, think of the situations where you will want this sprinkler system to go off before your emotional flames get out of control. The more you can anticipate frightening, angering, and stressful situations, the more effectively your subconscious mind will activate this system in time to prevent a blow-out. Finally, picture Spike installing an exhaust fan at one end of the building. When your sprinkler system goes off to put out a fire, there's likely to be a lot of smoke in the aftermath. That makes it hard to see reality. If you close your eyes and visualize this giant exhaust fan blowing away the smoke of anger, stress, and panic, you'll recover more quickly."

"Now we'll move into the heavy equipment zone. Here's an auxiliary-powered generator programmed to kick in when you need a boost of energy—like in mid-afternoon when you usually reach for the coffee. Next let's check out the furnace of desire—the old fire in the belly. We all have a furnace like that, but unfortunately in most people it's grown stone cold. The day you can visualize your furnace of desire and actually break out in a sweat is the day you become unstoppable."

"Now let's install one of my favorite pieces of industrial machinery—the electromagnet of universal awareness. Picture in your mind a giant, U-shaped magnet connected to a control panel with a keyboard. You can type in whatever you most need and once you've entered it, visualize a big power switch and see yourself turning it on. The electromagnet will begin to attract the help, the money, whatever it is you most need and have programmed into the control panel."

"One more stop, and it's the most important one: the control center. Imagine the thinking part of your brain as a magnificent computer. This afternoon, I'll show you how to program it with positive and affirming screen savers, but for now, let's visualize upgrading the memory and central processing unit. Imagine Spike installing new circuits and bigger disk drives."

"Now imagine you've entered the communications center. Up here, we need to install two vital pieces of equipment. First is a highly sensitive satellite dish to bring in signals from all over the universe. Even if you're not consciously paying attention, embedding this satellite dish in your subconscious will help you collect healthy and positive emanations from all around you."

"Equally important is the broadcast antenna. Picture something that looks like a short wave radio set. Anytime you find yourself hurting or in need of something, simply pick up the microphone and broadcast your plea — or if you prefer, your prayer — out into the universe, and believe that it will be guided to the person most able to help you."

"Just two more stops, but both of them are vitally important. First is your future scope. Imagine something that looks a lot like a periscope. Any time you feel overwhelmed by the daily press of events and lose sight of your ultimate goal, stop and relax for a moment, and imagine yourself sticking this scope way up high, above the chaos that seems to swirl all about you. Point it in the direction of your memory of the future, and the vision will help you keep your current circumstances in perspective."

"Finally, let's visit your navigation center. This contains two important devices. First a compass, keeping you pointed in the direction of your memory of the future. Any time your intuition tells you that you're getting off track, take a moment to visualize this compass. And last but not least, picture a flywheel, just like on the engine of a car, spinning around to keep your momentum going. Anytime you feel yourself losing momentum, visualize this flywheel, spinning 'round and round,' keeping you going during the times that Gollum would rather you give up."

Before concluding the morning session, Dr. Wellington took Charlie on a grand tour of his newly cleaned and remodeled attic. Together, they walked through the garden of his future dreams, inspected the walls to make sure that Gollum hadn't put up any new graffiti, polished the new self-image mirrors, and picked up the last few rock fragments from the boulder of fear that Ramrock and his crew had exploded. Then they double-checked all the new equipment they'd installed.

After lunch, Dr. Wellington gave Charlie mental routines for getting started in the morning, and for ending each day. He visualized Spike going through his attic, stoking up the furnace of desire, programming positive and affirming screen savers into his mental PC, reorganizing the boxes on the utility shelving, cleaning up the walls and polishing the mirrors.

At the end of the day, Dr. Wellington gave him several workbooks and a set of audiotapes. And a hug. "You're a winner, Charlie. The world really needs to have your dreams come true. Don't ever let Gollum get the upper hand, not ever again."

As Charlie walked to his car that evening, he saw another memory of the future. His organization would become a vehicle by which Dr. Wellington could share metaphorical visualization with millions of others. Charlie heard Gollum sniggering, then visualized Spike grabbing the little vandal by the scruff of the neck.

Charlie sat behind the wheel of his car and imagined himself getting ready for a big formula one race tomorrow. He was going to like using metaphorical visualization!

The Janitor In Your Attic

Predicators of success:
1. Fun
2. Faith
3. Repetition

Steps:
1. Remove doubt and fear
2. Construct infrastructure to handle anger, stress and panic

6

Make Fear Your Ally,
Make Adversity Your Teacher

AFTER LEAVING DR. WELLINGTON, CHARLIE WENT HOME TO DIG INTO HIS *Empowerment Pyramid Workbook*. Incorporating many of the insights he had learned from his trip to the Grand Canyon with Mitch Matsui and through his hyper-hypnosis session with Dr. Wellington, he was able to achieve a level of clarity previously inaccessible to him. Now, on one piece of paper, he had distilled a sense of purpose and direction that could serve as a guide for refining his own memories of the future.

The first block of the Empowerment Pyramid — IDENTITY — had yielded the biggest surprise. His real identity was totally incompatible with being a business consultant and corporate bureaucrat. He now realized that his authentic identity was much more as a crusader and as an entrepreneur.

The day he was working on his mission statement to include in the Pyramid's second block — MISSION — Charlie happened to read a cover article in *Fortune* magazine called "Finished at 40." It was about people just like him who, on the brink of their peak earning years, had been let go by their companies. Ironically, Charlie found himself feeling unsympathetic to the complaints of people worried about their houses and cars, six-figure paychecks, and 401(k) plans. If they spent less time worrying about money and more time figuring out how they could make a real contribution, they'd be much happier. In the long run, they'd probably be a lot richer to boot! These people need a support group, Charlie thought, an organized program that could teach them the skills to stop worrying about money, and to think big, dream big, and achieve big. Was it possible, he wondered, to build a successful business by creating programs of this type? He started writing, and after several drafts, had a mission statement:

> *My mission is to build a worldwide organization that gives people tools and resources that will help them create meaning and wealth in their lives and in the lives of others.*

Charlie had known he was on the right track when he shared it with Pam and she smiled and gave him a big hug. "Create the meaning and the wealth will create itself," she said, with a lot more confidence than Charlie felt at the time. But the mission excited him and he spent many hours working on a vision statement to implement it:

> *What would the world look like if I were becoming the person I am truly meant to be, and enthusiastically pursuing my real mission in life?*

Just as Dr. Wellington had predicted, when he tried to create a mental picture of his vision for the ideal future, the weeds of doubt began to cover it up. He was surprised at how effective his new "weedwhacker" was. The images had begun to flow more smoothly. In his mind, he saw a whole catalog with the types of products that had been helpful to him — like *The Janitor in Your Attic* and the *Empowerment Pyramid Workbook*.

Charlie envisioned groups of people meeting every week, all across the country, to support and encourage each other—and periodically, everyone coming together at huge conventions. Naturally, with his technical background, he also saw a big role for Internet-based programs.

Soon the vision was growing too fast for the weeds to keep up with it. Charlie saw himself leading groups of inward-explorers through the Grand Canyon, the same way Mitch Matsui had led him several months earlier. Youth programs, entrepreneurship festivals, summer success camps—Charlie smiled to think that Spike would have to add an additional aisle of shelving just to hold all the new boxes of ideas. The vision was beginning to be overwhelming, but the immediate steps were becoming crystal clear. Charlie would need help, and he would need money.

He found himself standing outside his bank. Earlier in the day, he'd signed a licensing agreement with Dr. Wellington to develop a family of products built around *The Janitor in Your Attic* theme, and had incorporated his company as The Courage Place, Inc. at his attorney's office. And several minutes ago, he had signed for the biggest loan he'd ever taken, pledging his personal assets as collateral.

Suddenly he felt like he was starting down a steep mountain on skis. There was no stopping or turning back. It was exhilarating. It was terrifying.

Charlie had no more appointments that day and the sun was shining, so he decided to take a walk. Feeling pulled to his right, he headed down the street. After several blocks, he felt a tug toward the left. After a few more turns, he realized he was headed toward the Downtown Gym, run by his old friend Nick Amatuzzo.

Nick had been a champion professional fighter. He'd also been an alcoholic and a drug addict. He'd known both the winning and losing sides of life. For the past twenty years, he'd put his heart and soul into the Downtown Gym. It had started as a haven for troubled boys, but later evolved into one of the city's most popular fitness clubs. Though he was now back on the winning side of life, Nick never forgot his days of trouble, and he never gave up on his commitment to his kids.

As he rounded the corner, Charlie saw the big sign over the gym's front window—the message that had drawn him there years ago:

Make Fear Your Ally
Make Adversity Your Teacher

Charlie saw Nick prowling through the weight room talking with clients. He knew he could expect a warm welcome. Not only were they good friends, but he and Pam had been among the gym's most generous supporters in its early days. Pam even picked Nick's kids up after school and gave them rides to the gym.

Eventually, Nick saw Charlie and walked over. "You're getting a little pudgy, there, marshmallow," he kidded, poking Charlie in the ribs. "Where's your gear? There's an exercise bike out there with your name on it."

"Not today, Nick. I'll come in over the weekend—promise. I actually have something serious I'd like to talk with you about."

Nick looked concerned. "Everything okay at home with Pam and the kids?"

"Yeah, Nick, everything's fine. It's really more about work. I got fired, you know. I don't work at LPI anymore."

"Gee, I hadn't heard that. How long ago?"

"Six weeks."

"Back in the workforce, huh? That's what happened to most of the guys here right now."

"Really?" Charlie guessed there were at least fifty people working out.

"Sure. Look at the clock." It was 3:15 in the afternoon. "A year, two years ago, most of these guys were sitting behind desks at some company downtown. Then one day, *Bang!* they get a pink slip and they're back in the workforce."

"You mean they're *out of* the workforce, don't you?"

Nick laughed. "Heck, no, I don't. What most of those guys were doing wasn't really work. They were sitting in boring meetings, writing memos, talking on the phone. Now, they're coming face-to-face with the fact that no one's gonna pay 'em to do that anymore. They're gonna have to start making something that someone else wants and then sell it to them at a profit, or they're gonna starve."

Nick looked into the weight room. "Look at 'em, Charlie, all pumped up and strutting around like Greek gods. And you know what? Inside, most of 'em are scared to death."

"So am I, Nick. Getting thrown out of the old comfortable workplace and into the workforce is the most terrifying thing I've ever been through."

Nick put an arm around Charlie's shoulders and started walking toward his office. Even though it had been over twenty years since Nick had been in the ring, he was still hard as steel. Charlie guessed that facing Nick in the ring would be far more terrifying than entering a competitive marketplace.

One whole wall of Nick's office was lined with pictures of famous fighters shaking hands with, or shaking a fist at, Nick. Dempsey, Ali, Hagler, both Sugar Rays, Forman and Fraser, and many others Charlie didn't recognize were there. In the place of honor behind Nick's desk, however, were pictures of men much less famous, but who owned the lion's share of Nick's heart: the boys he'd helped raise from juvenile delinquency to responsible adulthood.

Nick poured coffee as they sat at his small conference table. "So what's on your mind, Charlie?"

"I've decided to start my own business, Nick. I incorporated it today. It's called The Courage Place. I'm still working on the details, but it's going to be a membership organization that's part support group, part training center, and part adventure team."

"That's terrific, Charlie!" Nick beamed. "Heck, I bet we could walk out to the exercise room right now and sign up fifty guys. So what's bothering you?"

"The problem is that I'm scared to death."

"That's good, Charlie. Better scared than stupid! Most of the time I went into that ring I was scared. I could never make the fear go away, so I figured I might as well make friends with it. And I did. I made fear my ally."

"How do you do that?" Charlie asked. "Make fear your ally? How do you make adversity your teacher? If they're going to show up for the fight anyway, I'd sure like to have them in my corner."

"You've got the hard part figured out already, Charlie."

Charlie shook his head. "I'm not sure I understand, Nick."

"You've seen the young bulls out there with those t-shirts that say *No Fear*?" Charlie nodded, and Nick responded with a contemptuous snort. "No fear means no courage. Someone with no fear may be reckless, but they're not brave. No fear, no courage. Big fear, big courage!"

Nick sat back down again and drank some coffee. "Early in my fighting career, I developed my own formula for making fear my ally and for making adversity a teacher. I teach that formula to all these young people who come into the gym's youth program. I tried to get the local school system to build it into the curriculum, because too many kids are scared today, and no one's teaching them how to handle it." Nick shook his head and popped back out of the chair. "They laughed at me. Said it wasn't their job. But they're wrong; it darn well should be their job."

Nick picked up a book from his desk and tossed it to Charlie. "Have you read that yet?" Charlie shook his head. "Well, you should. It'll teach you how to worry well." Charlie read the cover—*Worry* by Edward R. Hallowell. "You know what he says is the biggest learning disability of all? Worse than dyslexia, worse than attention deficit disorder? Fear. When you're afraid, you don't learn. That's another reason why I have all my kids memorize the Never Fear, Never Quit Pledge. They complain at first, but in later years I've had them tell me it's the most important thing they've ever done."

Pulling a yellow pad in front of him, Nick sketched a square and a

THE NEVER FEAR, NEVER QUIT PLEDGE

❖ I will take full responsibility for my own happiness, for my own success, and for my own life.

❖ I will not blame other people for my problems, nor will I allow low self-esteem, self-limiting beliefs, or the negativity of others to talk me out of achieving what I am capable of achieving and becoming the person I am capable of being.

❖ I will have faith that, though I may not understand why adversity happens, by my conscious choice I can find strength, compassion, and grace through my trials.

❖ I will face rejection and failure with courage, aware-ness, and perseverance, making these experiences the platform for future acceptance and success.

❖ I will do the things I'm afraid to do, but which I know should be done. Sometimes this will mean asking for help to do that which I can't do by myself.

❖ I will earn the help I need in advance by helping other people now, and repay the help I receive by serving others later.

❖ When I fall down, I will get back up, whatever it takes.

❖ My faith in God and my gratitude for all that I have been blessed with will shine through in my attitudes and in my actions.

diamond. "The one thing you must never lose," he said, "is your hope. Here are the despair square and the hope diamond. The despair square is *despair* leading to *pessimism* leading to *inaction* leading to *failure*." Now he moved his pen to the diamond. "The hope diamond is *hope* leading to *optimism* leading to *action* leading to *success*. Without hope, it's hard to find courage."

"You also need energy. Courage without energy is nothing but good intentions. Energy without courage is as likely to run away as it is to stand and fight. That's why your business plan had better include renewing your membership in the Downtown Gym, Charlie! You better get in shape so you can have the energy to fight fear. Fear can be an ally if you subdue it, but if you don't, it will be the most deadly enemy you ever face."

Charlie smiled sheepishly. "I'll be in on Saturday with a check, Nick. But I'm not really sure what you mean when you say fear can be an ally. My fear always seems like the enemy."

"Fear can be an ally in four different ways," Nick responded. "First, it can simply be a warning that you're not ready for something. Whenever I climbed into the ring, the magnitude of my fear usually had more to do with how well I'd prepared than with the caliber of my opponent.

"When you're running a business, man, there's a lot to be afraid of. Of course, you can always run out of money. You can run out of time. You can get cheated by your employees. If you're not a good boss, you can end up cheating your employees."

"So you take an accounting course and discipline yourself to look at the books at the end of every day so you won't run out of money. That makes fear of bankruptcy your ally. You read a book on time management and you stop watching TV so you have time to watch your business. That makes fear of deadlines your ally."

"The second way fear can be an ally is it can tell you when you're on the wrong path in life. When your heart is pulling you in one direction, but your feet are following the paycheck in another, you're going to live with a lot of fear. I'm guessing that the last year or so at LPI you suffered from a sort of chronic dread. Am I right?"

"Knockout!" Nick smiled.

"That's because your heart didn't belong there, but your ego didn't want to believe it."

"You told me you were terrified when you walked out of the bank today, but you had the wrong diagnosis. What you were really feeling was the exhilaration of a new beginning. That's the magic that transforms fear into an ally."

"The third way fear can be an ally is when you recognize it as a call to action. When I had my shot at the title. I was scared, but I was also proud. I didn't just want to live through that fight, I wanted to win it. I trained like a monster. When the opening bell sounded that night in Madison Square Garden, I was faster and stronger and more confident than I'd ever been in my whole life."

"It went all fifteen rounds. My fear was transformed into an angry determination. I got beat pretty bad, Charlie, but I won the bigger fight. I won the respect of my fear. And we've had a pretty good relationship ever since."

Nick refilled both coffee cups. "The fourth way fear can be an ally is most important. Fear can be a call to faith. The things we're most afraid of, like dying, are things we really can't do anything about. So we make a choice. Do we face dying with fear or do we face it with faith?"

"Every time I went through those ropes into the ring, I crossed myself and left my life in God's hands. Today I'm afraid of different things. In business, it's things like rejection and failure we're afraid of, not getting a physical beating. But you know what? It's like I tell my kids. Rejection is like the red badge of courage. Cowards don't get rejected very often, because they don't even try."

"I've heard you talk about twelve steps of courage and perseverance, Nick. Can you tell me what they are?" Charlie was taking notes.

"There are six each—six steps for courage and six steps for perseverance."

"The first step to building courage is understanding your fear, to identify it. Let me give you an example. Johnny Dolan is one of the kids in our after-school program. He comes in the other day and shows me his report card. It's terrible! And he's afraid that his daddy's gonna give him a whippin'."

"So I asked him what the problem was. He says that his daddy's gonna whup him. No, I said, that's your *fear*. The *problem* is that you're not doing very well in school. I asked him to write down a list of things he could do to fix the problem — like spending more time studying instead of watching TV, or asking his teachers for help. Well, you wanna know what happened?"

Charlie nodded.

"When Johnny showed his daddy that report card *plus* his plan of action for making it better the next time, not only did he not get a whippin', but his daddy actually took him right down to the office supply store to buy him a new organizer. Fear is imaginary, so you can't really make it go away. But problems are real. You can fix them, and then fear becomes your ally."

"The second step is to talk to your fear, to understand what it's trying to tell you. When I decided to expand, to go from being just a gym for tough street kids to being an upscale health club, it was the scariest time of my life. I'd wake up in the middle of the night with a knot in my stomach. Finally, I decided to have a conversation with my fear, ask it what the problem was."

"You know what my fear told me?"

"What?"

"That my laziness was going to get me into big trouble. See, up to that point I had just assumed that running a health club would be pretty much like running a gym, but on a bigger scale. But my subconscious mind, and the fear it was creating, wasn't so sure. It wanted me to do some market research, maybe hire a consultant, before I started pouring my life savings into a new building. You know what happened to my fear when I started doing all those things?"

"It went away?"

"Where have you been for the last hour!" Nick bellowed. "Fear *never* goes away. It became my ally. Whenever I'd feel the fear come back again, I talked to it. You'll be amazed at how cowardly fear can be when you stand up to it."

"The third step is to get connected. The feeling of being alone against the world can be one of the most frightening experiences. When I was a fighter, I had a whole team in my corner, and I had a coach. I still do have a coach. Only now, it's a business coach. I spend four or five hours every week networking, meeting new people and building better relationships with people I already know."

"Who's your coach," Charlie asked, "and what are some of the groups you belong to?"

"You ever hear of Ryan Bennett?"

"The billionaire?"

"Yeah. Pretty amazing, how a guy turned a business he started in his bedroom into a billion dollar empire."

"Yep. Well, back when he was just getting started, he had this coaching program. He'd meet with a group of us every month, critique our business plans, and mostly just give us the kick in the ass we all needed to get moving. Now he's got a whole team of people he's trained to be coaches. And I've stayed with the program."

"Don't you ever reach a point where you don't need it anymore?"

"Charlie, think of the greatest professional athletes who ever played in any sport: Ali, Joe Montana, Flo-Jo, Michael Jordan, Cathy Rigby. Name any one of them who got so good she didn't need a coach anymore. Just one."

Charlie was silent.

"No matter how good you think you are or how much you think you know, one of the best investments you can make is having a good coach in your corner."

"After you get connected to *people,* the fourth step is to become detached from *things.* The more attached you are to your possessions, your lifestyle, your job, the more you set yourself up for living with the fear that you might lose those things."

"Be thankful for what you have when you have it, but don't mourn the loss if you should lose it."

"There are a lot of people in this gym today who say they would give their eye teeth to do what you're doing—start their own business. But they're not willing to pay the price, to give up the big house and the luxury car. They've become prisoners of their possessions. No wonder fear is never far below the surface in their lives."

"Step number five is to lighten up and have more fun. It's hard to be frightened when you're laughing."

"When I decided to expand in the health club business, I used to hate making cold calls to sell memberships. And because I hated it, I wasn't any good at it. I knew I had to find a way to make it fun. Well, you know me, I get a kick out of giving people a hard time. So I just started doing what comes naturally to me. Walking up to people and insulting them."

Charlie looked aghast and Nick just laughed.

"I'd walk up to some potbellied businessman waiting for a cab and say, 'Hey, fatso, why don't you get in shape so you can get a life.' Then I'd hand him a card for a free one-month membership at the gym."

"You didn't!"

"Sure did! Pretty soon I was the talk of the town. I was on all the TV news shows. Even had *Sports Illustrated* wanting to do a story about me, but they backed off when I called the publisher to tell him what a rotten thing it was for a sports magazine read by almost every kid in America to be pushing smoking the way it does."

"Did anyone ever pick a fight with you?"

"Hell, no! Would you start a fight with some guy wearing a Golden Gloves t-shirt and this face?"

"No way!" Charlie exclaimed.

"The last thing, point number six, is that you've got to have faith.

Like I said earlier, the biggest fears aren't so much conquered as they are accepted. When you have faith in the meaning of life and in the benevolent hand of the Creator, you begin to see how the things you're most afraid of are really to your ultimate benefit."

Nick stood and stretched.

"And that brings me to the second half of the formula — making adversity your teacher. The first step is simply to expect it. When something bad happens, don't feel as if somehow bad things should only happen to other people."

"The second step, though, is to realize that even though we must eventually all go *through* adversity, we don't need to wallow around in it."

"The third step is to see adversity as an advertisement for opportunity. The rainstorm that ruins a picnic also brings flowers and rainbows."

"You know, after people get fired, they spend a lot of time down here working out. I think it's a way they can get away from their problems. At first they're all really depressed, like it's the worst thing in the world. When I see them a couple of years later and ask how things are going, what do you think they say about having lost the old job?"

"It was the best thing that ever could have happened?"

"One hundred percent of the time. And that gets me to the fourth step. It's from the title of a book by Father Michael Crosby: *Thank God Ahead of Time*. No matter what happens to you, there's always something to be thankful for."

"The fifth step is to stay grounded in the present, to be thankful for what you have instead of agonizing over what you've lost. When I don't appreciate today, tomorrow is not as good either."

"Number six is to recognize apparent failure in the middle. When you get started on some new project, everybody's all excited and your success seems assured. After the final bell has rung, you know whether you won or lost. But in the middle things can get pretty chaotic. Sometimes the only difference between winners and losers is that the losers quit rather than work their way through the chaos."

"You've got to keep moving, Charlie. You've got to do those things you don't want to do."

"I always think of the 3-P's of perseverance. They are Purpose, Passion, and Patience. That's what Never Quit is all about. Know what your purpose is, be passionate about it, and be willing to be passionate for as long as it takes to make the vision become real."

Nick got up and walked over to his desk and pulled a small pad out of the top drawer. "Speaking of doing things you don't want to do," he said, "this is a gift certificate for our pro-shop. I want you to go over there right now and cash it in for some shoes, shorts, and a t-shirt. Then get your fat ass out there into the exercise area and go to work."

Nick waved his arms as if to sweep Charlie out of the room. "While you're out there, talk to as many people as you can about this idea of yours for a courage place. I'd be real interested in starting one here."

Twenty minutes later, Charlie was peddling an exercise bike wearing a new bright yellow Downtown Gym t-shirt. Turning to the person on the bike next to him, he smiled and asked, "So, how long have you been out of work?"

The other man shot back a surprised look. "How did you know that?"

Charlie smiled. He had the feeling he might have just recruited his first customer for The Courage Place.

DESPAIR SQUARE: DESPAIR LEADING TO PESSIMISM
LEADING TO INACTION LEADING TO FAILURE

HOPE DIAMOND: HOPE LEADING TO OPTIMISM LEADING
TO ACTION LEADING TO SUCCESS

Fear as an ally:
1. As a warning that you're not ready for something
2. Telling you you're on the wrong path
3. A call to action
4. A call to faith

FORMULA FOR MAKING FEAR YOUR ALLY
AND ADVERSITY YOUR TEACHER

Steps for courage
1. Identify and understand your fear
2. Understand what your fear is trying to tell you
3. Get connected with people
4. Detach from your possessions
5. Lighten up and have fun
6. Have Faith

Steps for perseverance
1. Expect adversity
2. Move on from adversity
3. See the opportunities in adversity
4. Be thankful for the blessings adversity will bring
5. Stay grounded in the present
6. Keep moving and work your way through the chaos of apparent failure in the middle

7

THINK BIG, START SMALL

"MOST OF THE PEOPLE I KNOW WHO CALL THEMSELVES ENTREPRENEURS aren't entrepreneurs at all—they're still employees. Often, they're employees with high risk, high hassle, low pay jobs, working for bosses who are so demanding and unreasonable that almost anyone else would have quit a long time ago. Those bosses are themselves."

Dr. Jared Mitchell was a true entrepreneur. While still a surgery resident at the University of Michigan, he had developed a regimen of vitamin and mineral supplements that seemed to help many of his patients recover quickly after surgery. Although it took a long time for the mainstream medical establishment to accept him and his insistent calls for doctors to pay more attention to nutrition, emotional health, and spiritual faith in the healing process, he quickly gained a following among the younger residents and medical students.

"Contrary to what most people think," he continued, "real entrepreneurs are not particularly concerned with making a lot of money. It's a nice by-product of their success, and more important, it's the fuel they need to keep building their dreams. But it's not the end goal in itself. The thing that drives the true entrepreneur is creating something of lasting value and leaving an enduring legacy."

Even before he'd finished his residency, Dr. Mitchell's Total Health Prescription, as it came to be known, sparked a quiet revolution within the hospital. Because there were no prescription drugs involved, it did not require a doctor's order. Therefore, anyone could recommend it to a patient. Increasingly, nurses, residents, even medical students were doing just that. Mitchell began packaging his "prescription" in a simple box containing seven bottles of pills, a book, and several audiotapes. He priced it at $18.95, and in the first month sold over a thousand of them.

By the time Mitchell had finished his residency, his company was selling over a million dollars a year of Dr. Mitchell's Total Health Prescription. This was especially remarkable because it was being done with no advertising, no sales force, and no retail presence. It was all by word of mouth.

"After sales took off in those first couple of months, I knew we had tapped into something huge. I even had some of the drug companies come along asking about licensing the system. It was quite an ego builder. In fact, that was my biggest challenge in those early days — keeping a reign on my ego so I didn't get carried away and grow too fast. I had a big sign printed up that I hung in my office which read:

THINK BIG
START SMALL

Charlie had noticed the sign when he came into Dr. Mitchell's office. He'd been referred by Wilma Osterberge, a Saint Johns classmate who was now one of the top distributors for Body Spirit, the name Mitchell had chosen for his company. Charlie had read everything he could about Jared Mitchell and Body Spirit. This was a meeting that could put The Courage Place on the map.

"When the drug companies tried to buy me out, the two things they promised were promotion and delivery systems. But the price I would have had to pay was a total loss of my independence. I could have made a lot of money, but I would have no longer been an entrepreneur. I went out and hired a big-time consultant, someone who specialized in business strategy. He came back with a report that essentially said the only way I could avoid being eaten alive by the drug companies, who could have quite easily developed their own product line, was to grow as big as possible as fast as possible. That brilliant advice cost me twelve grand."

"So what did you do?" Charlie asked.

"What any good entrepreneur would do—the exact opposite of what he recommended. For the next year, I went underground. I deliberately downplayed the product, even made it difficult to find."

"Why'd you do that?"

"Two reasons. First, I wanted any potential competitor to think I'd crashed and burned. I even hired a publicist to plant stories in the pharmaceutical trade press about how I'd had to lay off half of my employees, which was a real joke, because back then I didn't have any employees. But they bought it hook, line, and sinker. The buy-out offers went away, but so did the threat of being stomped out before I could get my roots down."

"My company lost over a hundred thousand dollars that year, but it was the most profitable year of my life," he continued. "I interviewed hundreds of patients who had used my system, and the doctors and nurses who had recommended it. What worked? Why did they like it? How could I make it better? I hired a student from the art school to help me design better packaging, and kept working on making the formula more effective."

"I studied the most successful companies and imitated the practices that made them great. I started recruiting key opinion leaders like they do at Nike and promoting a culture of fun and pride like they've built at Southwest Airlines — I took the best from the best."

"But the most important thing I did was study the companies that were successful in direct consumer marketing. Companies like Amway and Mary Kay were revolutionizing product promotion and distribution with the oldest form of commerce: coming to you and saying 'Hey, Charlie, I used this product and it really works. Why don't you give it a try?' Then you try it, you like it, you share it with someone else, and our network grows."

"That's how I would organize my business. I didn't need professional sales reps and I didn't need a slick ad campaign. My customers would be my sales force, and my product would be its own advertisement. I recruited five of my best supporters and rented a cabin for a week. I taught them all about the product, how to sell it, how to recruit other distributors. We talked about the incentives and compensation systems being used by all the various companies out there, and picked the elements we liked best to design our own. Today, those five people are all multi-millionaires. And they're all just as involved today as they were in the early years."

"It took another nine months before we were ready to really start building the business. We had to develop computer programs, build up a product inventory and a system to manage it, and a million other things. I was on the road pretty much non-stop. By deliberately staying small, we were able to build the foundation on which all of our future success would be built. And we've held onto that philosophy. You know how some multi-level marketing companies promise untold wealth in ninety days or less?"

Charlie smiled. His fax machine spit out offers like that all day long.

"Well, we promise our new distributors that it absolutely will not happen to them. During their first year with the company, they are allowed to recruit only five new people." Mitchell smiled. "Hey, it worked for me, and I believe in staying with what works. Anyway, during that year, we expect them to spend a lot of time with their sponsor learning about Body Spirit — and not just our products, but our philosophy and our values. Then we expect them to spend just as much time working with the five people they have sponsored, teaching them the same things."

"We ask an awful lot of them in the first year, and they're hardly making any money at all. But by the end of that year, they have built a team that is ready for explosive growth."

Mitchell picked up a folder. "I've read your proposal, Charlie, and I'm intrigued. I think you're really on to something here. The Courage Place is a terrific concept and I'd like to help you. I'm just not sure how we can do it."

"It's the old brush off," Charlie heard Gollum say.

Mitchell pulled a business card from his shirt pocket and handed it to Charlie. "Bill Keys is one of my original five. Now he's down in Austin, Texas. I hope you don't mind, but I took the liberty of faxing him a copy of your proposal, and he was just as intrigued as I am. He said that if you can't get something like that going in Austin, which is a very progressive community, then your idea is DOA — dead on arrival. Won't work anywhere. But if you can get it going in Austin, he's pretty sure that Dallas and Houston will fall in line, with San Antonio coming on next. After that, there's probably a dozen smaller cities like El Paso and Galveston where he can see it working."

"If you really want to make this happen, Bill Keys will pick up his sword and shield and stand there beside you. But if you're only at ninety-nine percent, don't waste his time or yours. Go back to the drawing boards and keep working until you are at one hundred and ten percent."

"How will I know?" Charlie asked.

"Terrific question! The answer depends upon how much of a price you're willing to pay. There's a paradox: starting small will require a massive effort on your part. If Bill pledges his team to your support, are you willing to do *whatever it takes*," and Mitchell emphasized each of the last three words, "to make The Courage Place-Austin a model for your success everywhere else? Are you willing to sign a one-year lease on a studio apartment in Austin so you can go down there for weeks at a time? Are you willing to spend every breakfast, lunch, dinner, and coffee break spreading your enthusiasm for the project? Are you willing to buy yourself a pair of snakeskin cowboy boots and develop a taste for Lone Star beer? In other words, to do *whatever it takes.*"

"I don't know," Charlie said at last.

"Good," Mitchell replied. "That's the answer I was hoping to hear. That means you're *thinking*. When I say 'think big,' too many people hear the word 'big' but don't hear the word 'think.' The thinking is the first step. Why don't you give Bill a call and see if you can set up a time to go down and meet with him and some of the members of his team? I think you'll find it very helpful."

Charlie nodded, sensing the interview was near its end.

"By the way," Mitchell said, "you won't have to rent an apartment in Austin. Bill has a guest house that I'm sure he'd be more than happy to let you use any time you're down there. Which I hope will be a lot. It's big enough that you can take your family with you if it doesn't interfere with the kids' school."

Mitchell stared at Charlie. "Your business plan is risky, Charlie. Nobody has ever made anything quite like this work before." He paused, for a moment, then smiled.

"That's why I like it. It's unique and it's daring, and I believe you can pull it off. I want to help you because your success will be good for Body Spirit. But most of all, I want to help you because you're setting out to do something very important. There are a lot of frightened people, hurting people, out there, who are so blinded by their fears they don't see the opportunities all around them. The Courage Place could be a sort of health club for the soul. I think you'll make a big difference in this world."

Mitchell looked at his watch and stretched. Charlie couldn't believe it was almost noon, and that one of America's most successful entrepreneurs had just given him three hours from a crazy schedule. Charlie pushed forward in his chair, preparing to leave.

"I've got to catch a plane for L.A.," Mitchell said, "but I'm not going anywhere on an empty stomach. Can I buy you lunch downstairs? If

you've got the time, I'd like to share with you some of the basic principles of the Think Big, Start Small philosophy. It's not as simple as it
seems."

"If *I've* got the time," Charlie exclaimed. "You're the one whose got
to be in six cities in the next five days! I'd be grateful for your advice,
but at least let me buy lunch."

"Whatever," Mitchell replied.

Mitchell led Charlie to The Burger Bar, a little restaurant in the
lobby of his building. "The usual, Jerry?"

"Sure, April, but could you tell Wally to put real peppers on this
one, not those wimpy pickle slices he used last time?"

"Sure thing," the waitress replied. "And how about for you, honey,"
she said, looking at Charlie. "Well, I guess I'll have the same," he
replied.

"Good grief, another lunatic. Where do you dig these guys up,
Jerry?" Without waiting for a response, she walked back toward the
kitchen.

"What have I gotten myself into?" Charlie asked.

"Oh, it won't be so bad," Mitchell replied. "Just a grilled ham and
cheese with a big wad of jalepeno peppers in it."

As they ate, Mitchell outlined what he called the ten commandments of Think Big, Start Small. "The first commandment is to start
with yourself. I would guess that, when you think of the person you
would ideally like to become, there's a pretty big gap between that
ideal and where you are today."

"Oh, not too big," Charlie replied. "I'd say it's bigger than the
Grand Canyon but smaller than the Pacific Ocean." Both men smiled,
and Mitchell said, "Keep it that way, Charlie. The day you think
you've arrived, you've lost the game."

Mitchell pulled a card out of his wallet and handed it to Charlie.
"These are the Twelve Core Action Values of Never Fear, Never Quit.
Have you ever heard of it?"

"Well, Nick Amatuzzo at the Downtown Gym gave me a copy of

the Never Fear, Never Quit Pledge, but this is the first I've ever seen of these values. May I make a copy?"

"Why don't you just keep the card. I work my way through that list every year. It's an idea that I believe was originated by Ben Franklin, to take one virtue per month and apply yourself to it. This is the third month in the cycle, so for me it's Perseverance month. That's why I'm spending so much time on the road. I'm going after the potentially big clients who have turned us down to see if one more big push won't bring us the business."

"The second commandment is that thinking comes before getting rich. But every day I meet people who have it reversed. They think they don't have the time to think because they're too busy trying to make a living. It's like putting up a building first, and then going back to draw the blueprints. You've got to pay attention, see the opportunities that everyone else is walking right past, ask the questions that everyone else is afraid to ask. Then you start thinking in ways that no one else is thinking. That's when you start walking down the road to becoming rich."

Mitchell asked the waitress to bring another bowl of jalepeno peppers, saying with a wink that they kept him young. "Third, recognize the paradox that while what will be big tomorrow might seem small today, what seems big today will be small tomorrow. The tiny mustard seed will, with care, grow into a tree. But at the same time, the mountain that seems so big today will eventually reveal itself as just a foothill on the path toward even more magnificent towers that were previously hidden in the mist."

"The fourth commandment is to start small, but to start now. Right now! To be an entrepreneur is to make lots of mistakes. Try things. Pursue what works and abandon what doesn't work."

"Have you ever read any of the work of James Bryan Quinn? He's a professor at the business school at Dartmouth College."

"No," Charlie replied.

"Well, about twenty years ago, Quinn did some research that

showed the most successful business strategies weren't developed at some management retreat, but evolved out of small marketplace experiments. He called it Logical Incrementalism, which is perhaps another way of saying Think Big, Start Small. At Body Spirit, we're pretty picky about who we bring on board. We probably interview a hundred people for every one we bring under our wing. Now, how big do you think our company would be today if, instead of flying around the country talking to people all day every day, I'd sat in my office drawing up plans for how to snag exactly the right people?"

Charlie just shook his head.

"A whole lot smaller. And that's a metaphor for the fifth commandment. You have to go start prying open those oysters. Not very many of them will have pearls in them, but the sooner you start opening them, and the more of them you open, the more pearls you will find."

"Number six is to dream like a king, but spend like a pauper. Especially in the early days of business, you've got to be a real curmudgeon. At some point, you're going to run out of money. That must be one of the ironclad laws of entrepreneurship, like running out of money is some sort of cosmic test you have to pass to graduate from the survival stage to the growth stage. And when you do run out of money, you're going to think back on all the money you've blown and wish you had it back in the bank."

"Number seven is another paradox. You need to be absolutely committed to your mission, but detached from the outcome. From the very beginning, you have to keep that vision of where you're going — I think you earlier referred to it as your memory of the future — planted firmly in the front of your mind. It has to be a total commitment, that you will do *whatever it takes* to make that vision, that memory of the future, become a reality."

"But at the same time, you have to be flexible about how you get there. There will be many apparent setbacks, some of which will be genuine reversals and others which will turn out to be blessings in disguise. It's almost always impossible to tell one from the other when you're in the middle of it. You have to have the equanimity to accept the circumstances, without abandoning your central purpose."

"I have a friend whose business was forced into bankruptcy, substantially as a result of outside forces over which he had little control. At the time, it was devastating. But if you ask him today, he'll tell you that bankruptcy was the best thing that ever happened to his business. It got him more focused on his priorities, and forced him to compensate for his own weaknesses by building a stronger management team. Once he did that, though, he was able to start dreaming even bigger dreams.

"The eighth principle is that you need to be very careful about who you select to be part of your original core team. Today, Body Spirit has over 100,000 marketing execs around the world, but guess how many are involved in making the most important decisions. The handful of people who were with me from the very beginning. They're not necessarily any smarter or more capable than the others, they just happened to be there when we were building the foundation."

"It's going to be much the same with The Courage Place. You'll always have a special relationship with the people who set up your first few shops, with those first few investors who believed in you and your dream when no one else would. Choose those first few people very carefully, Charlie, then take very good care of them, because they will be crucial to your success."

"I can't think of anyone who built a more enduring legacy than Jesus of Nazareth. Two thousand years after His death, more than a quarter of the world's population looks to Him as their savior. He built this church on the foundation of twelve men He hand-picked for the job."

"Commandment number nine is to avoid negative people and petty thinkers. They will bring you down, they will steal your dreams. When the going gets tough, and it most assuredly will, they will stand over you gloating. Go out of your way to be with people who have big dreams of their own and believe in their ability to fulfill those dreams. Those are the people most likely to see the beauty in your big dreams, and to help you achieve them."

"Number ten is more practical, and that's to build a growth contingency into your every plan. When I was a resident, I served on the hospital Facility Planning Committee. We were designing a new building, and the architect had marked a 'shell space.' There was nothing in it. He said it was designated for future growth. At the time, no one knew what that growth would be, but it was a lot cheaper to build the shell without finishing the interior than it would have been to add on later."

"When you start your business, build in some shell space. Hire people who are more qualified than they need to be, so they can grow into jobs you may not have anticipated. Get a computer system bigger and faster than you think you'll need. Do all this within reason, of course. The investment will pay off."

"Those are my ten commandments of Think Big, Start Small, Charlie. Just one more word of advice. Don't just start small. Enjoy the small things. If you're not enjoying the journey, the destination will be a disappointment."

"Speaking of destinations," Mitchell said as he rose, "I've got a plane to catch. You can buy me lunch next time. They'll just put this one on my tab."

Charlie walked with Mitchell out to the parking lot and watched him climb into a new BMW Roadster. As he drove off, Charlie read the license plate: TBSS.

THE TWELVE CORE ACTION VALUES OF NEVER FEAR, NEVER QUIT

1. **Authenticity**
    Know who you are and what you want; master your ego, emotions, and ambitions; and believe yourself capable and deserving of success.

2. **Courage**
    Make fear your ally and always act with confidence and determination.

3. **Perseverance**
    Make adversity your teacher and never give up on your dreams.

4. **Vision**
    Dream magnificent dreams, transform them into memories of the future, plan for their fulfillment, and keep the dream alive when the going gets tough.

5. **Mission**
    Define your purpose in life and perform your work with love and enthusiasm.

6. **Enthusiasm**
    Pursue your mission with passion, bring joy into the lives of others, and have fun in what you do.

7. **Focus**
    Concentrate your essential resources on your key priorities and avoid distractions.

8. **Awareness**
    Keep your attention anchored in the present here and now, and keep it centered on the positive.

9. **Service**
    Share your blessings, help others succeed, and have a compassionate heart.

10. **Integrity**
    Be honest with yourself and others, honor your commitments, and be humble.

11. **Faith**
    Believe that you will be supported in ways that cannot be anticipated or explained, and expect a miracle.

12. **Leadership**
    Ask for help, build a team, help each team member be a winner, and create an enduring legacy.

TEN COMMANDMENTS OF THINK BIG, START SMALL:

1. Start with your own personal development
2. Thinking comes before getting rich
3. What will be big tomorrow might seem small today ... what seems big today will be small tomorrow
4. Start now
5. Don't stop
6. Dream like a king, spend like a pauper
7. Commit to your mission, detach from its outcome
8. Select your original team of workers very carefully
9. Avoid negative people
10. Build a growth contingency into every plan

8

BE THE GREATEST
BEFORE YOU'RE THE GREATEST

TERRY ROBERTSON WAS THE GREATEST SALESMAN CHARLIE KNEW. HE'D BEEN class president at Saint Johns the year before Charlie started. In his first years out of school, Terry became one of the top salespeople for a large national computer company. When they cut back his territory because he was making too much money, he quit and bought a chain of failing furniture stores. Seven years later he sold it to a larger chain for a sum impressive enough to be reported in *The Wall Street Journal*. After deciding he wasn't quite ready for retirement, he'd bought an auto dealership which had slipped from first to nearly last in its market, and was on the verge of going under.

"I don't know, Charlie," he said as they walked through his used car lot. "I'm either crazy or I'm a challenge-aholic. When someone tells me that something can't be done, it's almost like showing a red flag to a bull. Something in me just has to prove them wrong."

Ten months earlier, Charlie had opened The Courage Place in his home city by renting space from Nick Amatuzzo at the Downtown

Gym. True to his word, Nick had helped him start the ball rolling by personally bulldozing many of his members into the program. Charlie had also been helped by lots of free publicity, including a visit by the governor, who said that The Courage Place was one of the most important examples of "entrepreneurship with a conscience" happening in the state.

Things were going so well that Charlie decided to open The Courage Place-Austin six months ahead of schedule. Bill Keys had helped him find a facility, and signed up as a member himself, but then gradually drifted out of the picture as he felt the pull of his responsibilities with Body Spirit. After an initial surge of interest prompted by the same type of free publicity he had received back home, the phone had gone deathly silent. He was only half joking when he suggested to his local manager that she go around insulting people the way Nick Amatuzzo had in order to build his health club business.

So, he was in an anxious frame of mind when he took his car to Richardson Automotive for service. Since the dealership was only a mile from the public library, Charlie had planned to walk over and do some research until they had his car finished. On his way out the door, he had run into Terry.

"Charlie McKeever. Just the man I've been looking for!" As always, Terry looked like a million dollars. His blue suit coat was perfectly tailored and sported a fresh red rose in the lapel. He strode across the showroom floor as if he owned the place, which of course he did. "If you've got a minute, I'd like to show you something," Terry said, pulling Charlie toward his office.

"Sure, Terry," Charlie said, "but I can only take a minute. There's a bunch of work I need to do over at the library."

"The library! What the heck are you doing in the library on a day like this? It's a beautiful day, and that means people are in the mood to buy something! Why on earth would you want to use your prime selling hours sitting in the library?"

They stepped into Terry's office, which was filled with car books, models, and posters. "Sit down. Just for a minute, Charlie, I want to show you something." Charlie's eyes were arrested by a poster of a classic red Ferrari. It had always been the car of his dreams.

Terry handed Charlie a photo of a brand-new white sports utility vehicle which had The Courage Place logo on the sides. "Where did you get this?" Charlie demanded. "That logo is our trademark. Who's driving this thing around, anyway?"

Terry didn't answer, but instead smiled and leaned forward, and in his best used car salesman impression said, "Imagine how many Courage Place memberships you'd sell, Charlie, if it was *you* driving this thing around town."

When Charlie didn't smile, Terry continued, "I really believe in what you're doing, which is why I had the fellas down in the graphics shop make this up on the computer. We can work out some sort of trade where you give memberships to The Courage Place to my people, and I'll give you a big discount on the vehicle. Behind the wheel of this thing, you'll become the salesman of the century!"

Charlie shook his head. "This is very nice, Terry, but you know, I'm really not much of a salesman. I've got a lot of other strengths, but that's just not one of them."

Terry widened his eyes and let his jaw drop in a look of mock amazement. "If you're not the salesman for The Courage Place, Charlie, who is?"

Charlie squirmed in his chair, wishing he was sitting in his favorite cubicle at the library. He'd planned on today being what he called a monastery day — a day where he squirreled away all alone with his books and his thoughts. Instead, Terry was trying to pull him back into the push-and-shove world of business — and of selling.

Terry walked around behind his desk, opened the drawer, took out a set of keys and dropped them into his coat pocket. Then he walked back around, looked up at the red Ferrari on the wall, and back down at Charlie. "There are two kinds of people in the world, Charlie.

People who are in sales, *know* they're in sales, take it seriously, and get good at it. Those people tend to get what they want out of life — they're the ones who live the biggest dreams." Now Terry looked over at a poster of a small family sedan. "And then there are people who *are in sales but think they're not*. They would never think of reading a book on sales strategy or listen to a tape on the most effective ways to close a sale. And they wonder why they're not getting what they want out of life."

"You *are* in sales, Charlie. Whether you are promoting The Courage Place, raising money for the symphony, or trying to teach a certain set of values to your children, you *are* in sales. For sure, you can hire other people to help you with it, but in the end, if you are not selling, nobody else will."

Charlie knew that Terry was speaking the truth, and it made him acutely uncomfortable.

"You know what selling is, Charlie? Selling is the ultimate test of self-esteem. When you get right down to it, you only have one product to sell: yourself. And you really only have one customer to sell to. It's a tough, cynical, ornery, and negative customer: yourself. If you can sell you on yourself, you can sell dirt to a farmer. Until you make that critical first sale, business is going to be a struggle for you."

Terry stared at the poster of the Ferrari until Charlie's eyes followed. "It's a beautiful car, isn't it, Charlie?"

Charlie laughed. "I'd give my eye teeth to see that in my driveway."

"Would you, Charlie? Would you really?" Before Charlie could answer, Terry walked over to the office door, motioning for Charlie to follow. "I want you to see something," he said.

As they walked out into the sun, Terry pointed to a sparkling white sport utility vehicle mounted at an angle on a display platform, as though it were climbing a steep hill. "That's your SUV," he said. "All we have to do is put the graphics on it. Can't you just see it, Charlie? Parked out in front of your office? A billboard on wheels! I had my guys set it up out here when I learned you'd be coming in today."

Charlie was amazed. "How'd you know I'd be in today?"

"Every night before I go home, I check the service log for the following day. If I see someone I know, I make a point of dropping in to say hi. You'd be amazed at how many cars I sell that way."

"I hope I don't disappoint you if I don't buy a car today," Charlie said.

"You won't disappoint me if you don't buy a car, Charlie," Terry laughed. "You'll disappoint me if you don't buy two of them."

Charlie didn't have time to protest, because Terry was already making a beeline for the used car lot. "Actually, Terry, I'm not in the market for any cars, much less two of them." Terry stopped cold in his tracks, wheeled around to face Charlie, stuck his right fist high in the air, and at the top of his lungs shouted, "I AM THE GREATEST!"

Charlie stood stunned, not sure whether his friend was going crazy or had just attended a seminar on outrageous sales techniques.

"Who's the first person that comes to your mind when you hear those words, 'I am the greatest?'"

"Mohammed Ali."

"Did he start saying it before or after he officially became the greatest by beating Sonny Liston to win the world title?"

"Probably before."

"That's right," Terry said. "In fact, today he'll tell you that he started saying it before even he believed it was true. It's got to happen in your head and in your heart before it happens in the world outside." As they kept walking towards the used car lot, Terry continued his lesson on salesmanship. "When you get right down to it, success in sales requires only two things: preparation and expectation. Anticipate the needs of your customer and put together a package, then present the package in a way that cannot be refused."

On the far end of the used lot, Charlie could see that Terry had already expanded the business. A large sign announced his new imports and exotics lot. "Want me to tell you why I know you're going to buy a new car today?" Terry asked. Charlie decided to go with it. "Why's that, Terry?"

"Because when I learned that you'd be coming in today, I didn't sit down and ask myself 'How can I sell my old friend Charlie a new car?' Instead, I read up on what you've been up to for the past few years. I learned as much as I could about The Courage Place, including how fast it took off here and the struggles you've been having in Austin." When Charlie shot him a surprised look, Terry said, "The Internet can be a salesman's best friend. Simply by investing a few minutes I was able to read everything both local and Texas papers had said about you and your business over the past year."

"So what do you think was the first thing I did this morning?" Charlie shrugged. "I stopped by the Downtown Gym and signed up as a member of The Courage Place. While I was there, I picked up a few of your brochures and brought them back to the office. I took them down to our paint shop and asked the graphics technician to superimpose your logo on a photo of that new sport utility vehicle you're going to buy today," and with that Terry gave Charlie a playful punch on the shoulder. "The monthly payments on your new SUV are going to be one third what you're paying for the billboard on Broadmore Street, and you're going to get a whole lot more visibility from it." When Charlie raised his eyebrows, Terry said, "Yeah, I checked that out too."

"So when we go back to my office, I'll go through all the details with you: the substantial discount you're going to get by signing all my people up as members of The Courage Place; the tax advantages of owning the vehicle through your corporation; and the superior quality graphics we're going to apply. But for now, let's have a little fun." In front of them, parked nose to the road, was a shiny red Ferrari. Terry tossed a set of keys to Charlie.

Charlie caught the keys fumbled them, and watched them bounce off his shoe onto the pavement. "I can't drive this thing," he said and was going to toss the keys back to Terry, but the salesman was already climbing into the passenger seat. "Let's go, Charlie, start 'er up."

Reluctantly, Charlie crawled in.

The leather seat seemed to mold itself around him, and for a fleeting second Charlie pictured himself writing a down-payment check. That image was quickly replaced by one of him trying to explain his new purchase to Pam.

"You've got to put the key in the ignition, Charlie. Otherwise it won't start."

"Generally, I find two kinds of people buy a car like this," Terry continued. "First are those with low self-esteem who need the status symbol to feel better about themselves. Second are people with high self-esteem who just love the thrill of driving the world's finest car."

"There's no way I should be driving a car this expensive, Terry. It costs more than my house does! What if we get in an accident?"

"That's what you've got insurance for. I'll tell you what—let's play a game. Let's pretend your business has been so successful that if you wanted to, you could just buy this car outright—pay cash for it. You know you're not going to buy it, because what you *really* want is that new sport utility vehicle with your logo all over it. But you decide as long as you're here, you might as well take it for a spin, since it's always been the car of your dreams."

"You're crazy," Charlie replied as he turned the key. "Seatbelts on?" he asked as he put the car in gear. Easing out Charlie turned right, heading for the countryside.

"You know," Terry said at last, "this new job of mine has given me a whole new perspective on the power of self-esteem. My salespeople who have high self-esteem make two or three times the money that salespeople with low self-esteem make, and without working any harder. If anything, they spend less time trying to sell because they're spending more time on building relationships. And customers who come in with high self-esteem always seem to spend less time choosing their cars, and end up getting a better deal."

Charlie was silent, so Terry continued. "In fact, I'd go so far as to say that low self esteem is one of the most debilitating diseases in our society today, and unfortunately it's at an epidemic level. I'm convinced that just helping people raise their self esteem would do more good for society and the economy than all the social welfare programs put together. Low self esteem is like emotional cancer: too often, it's an insidious excuse for cowardice and laziness. Because they don't think very highly of themselves, people assume they will be rejected, and that they will fail. So they don't even try. If you don't try to sell something, you won't be rejected. If you don't try to start something, you won't fail. The sad irony is that, because you know you've been a coward, you end up being rejected by the most important person of all—yourself; and by avoiding failure at a small level, you end up being a failure at the highest level."

Charlie looked down at the speedometer and realized with horror that he was going almost ninety miles per hour. The ride was so smooth he could hardly feel the speed. Quickly, he put his foot on the brake and slowed back down to the speed limit. In the other seat, Terry was looking at him and laughing. "What's so funny?"

"What you just did is such a terrific metaphor for low self-esteem," Terry replied.

"You mean speeding is a sign of high self-esteem?"

"Not at all," Terry replied. "What I mean is that low self-esteem is often reflected in fear of success. People get moving too fast in the direction of their goals and it scares them silly. So they back off the accelerator, put their foot on the brake, and fall back into their comfort zone."

"Have you heard our ads on the radio?" Terry asked. "Sure," Charlie replied, "you've really come up with a catchy jingle."

Terry pulled an audiocassette tape from his shirt pocket and plugged it into the car's tape player. When the announcer's voice came on, he was not selling cars—he was selling Terry Richardson. The ad was selling Terry, the natural-born entrepreneur; Terry the tough competitor; Terry, the customer service king; Terry, the wise and compassionate leader.

"Every person on our team has one of these tapes, courtesy of our ad agency. They asked us each to describe the ideal 'me,' and then made up the tape as though we had already arrived at that point."

"It's like I said. The starting point to success is selling yourself on yourself. In my business, advertising is like the fuel that keeps the car running. If I quit advertising the business would coast to a stop. Well, it's the same thing in our personal lives. You need a tape like this, Charlie, and you need to keep playing it until you believe that you really belong behind the wheel of this expensive sports car."

At the next town Charlie started heading back. Terry continued his lesson. "Whenever I hire a new salesperson, the first thing I do is teach him my formula for believing in yourself. The first step is understanding that faith in yourself occurs in four different dimensions."

"Four dimensions? Sounds like science fiction."

"Well, maybe so," Terry replied with a laugh, "but it's really just science."

"The first level of believing in yourself is what I call Self-Concept. In other words, what is your picture of the universe and your relationship to it?"

"The most successful salespeople have a tremendous faith in a loving God who wants them to succeed, and who occasionally will pull strings behind the scenes to help create the conditions for their success. On the other hand, people who view God as a punishing avenger are much less likely to build the foundation for long term success."

"The second dimension is Self-Image. What do you see when you look in the mirror? The greatest salespeople have a realistic appraisal of their own strengths and weaknesses, but when they look in the mirror, all they see are their strengths."

Terry looked down at the speedometer and smiled. "I see that success is beginning to be less of a terrifying prospect." Charlie realized with horror that he was going over one hundred miles per hour, and yet the car was riding so smoothly he might as well have been toodling down a city street. He took his foot off the gas and began coasting back down to the speed limit. As the owner of a struggling buisness, he couldn't afford a huge speeding ticket!

"The third dimension is Self-Esteem. Do you like what you see when you look in the mirror? I've seen people with what you would consider modest capabilities do very well simply because they like who they are. On the other hand, I've seen very talented people fail because they just can't seem to bring themselves to like the person who looks back at them from the bathroom mirror."

"Finally, the fourth dimension is Self-Confidence. Do you think you're up to the responsibilities life has laid out for you? Can you do the job? When I have a salesperson struggling with low self-esteem I spend time helping them build their confidence. You know, how to build rapport with customers, how to ask the right questions, how to find out what the customer can really afford, and how to close the sale. It's amazing what closing a few sales will do for someone's self-esteem and self-image. You want to know the best thing you can do right now?"

Charlie nodded. "Sure."

"Forget about going to the library to read books that tell you what you already know. Instead, start driving around town and paying personal visits to the CEOs of every company you can find, selling them corporate memberships to The Courage Place. Whether you close any sales or not will be less important than building your confidence as you polish your presentation."

"That's a great idea, Terry, but you're forgetting one minor detail. My car will be in your shop for the rest of the day."

"Actually, Charlie, the guys in the shop told me that your car has a lot more wrong with it than they thought. They're going to need it for the rest of the week. So this," and Terry patted the leather dashboard of the Ferrari, "will be your loaner car until next Monday."

"No way!"

"I'm afraid you'll have to make do with it, Charlie. And when you go around making your calls on CEOs, make sure you park right up front and gun the engine a few times before you get out. That will really get their attention!"

Charlie was about to argue when a little voice told him that this was a gift to be appreciated. So he simply said thanks.

They had just crossed back over the city limits when Terry pointed to the Golden Arches up ahead. "Let's pull in there. I'm starving!"

Charlie gunned the engine for a downshift, feeling more at home in the seat of the Ferrari. As he turned into the lot, he asked, "Do you want to go through the drive through?"

"Are you kidding! Eat cheeseburgers in a quarter-million dollar car!"

As they were eating lunch, Terry asked Charlie to look around the dining room and, based upon people's expressions, imagine what they were talking about.

"Let's see," Charlie said. "The young mother over there is telling her children to shape up or she'll stick them in the car. Those two workmen over there are talking about what a moron their supervisor is. Those two guys in suits, one is trying to sell a life insurance policy to the other, but it's not going very well. The guy sitting alone going through the want ads with a pencil got laid off a long time ago, and now he doesn't even have the energy to shave in the morning. Not a very happy lot, are they?"

"It's really sad how many people would rather wallow around in their problems than fix them. They'll sit in here and yell at the kids instead of taking a class on how to be a more effective parent. They're content to bitch and moan about their terrible job conditions instead of learning the skills that would earn them a better job. They're content to sit here reading the want ads day after day instead of having the courage to go start a little business. It's a paradox, Charlie. Sometimes the more discontented you are, the more likely you are to find the courage to make the changes that will bring you happiness."

"Would you gentlemen like refills on your sodas?" The attendant was an older woman with a neatly starched and pressed shirt, and a smile the size of Texas. Charlie wondered if she was working at McDonalds to keep herself busy, or because she had to in order to make ends meet. She returned momentarily, and placed the drinks on the table. "Isn't this a gorgeous day?" she asked, looking out the window. Then, lowering her voice slightly, continued, "Do you see that beautiful red sports car out there? Wouldn't that be a hoot to drive?" After she left, Terry said, "In one of his books, Bill Bennet said that there are no menial jobs, only menial attitudes. Truer words were never spoken."

"Before we head back to the dealership," Terry said, "let me share my formula for building solid self-esteem. There are three elements to having high self-esteem. First is to accept yourself as you are, warts and all. We've all got them, you know."

"The second element, however, is a willingness to change, to fix the warts. Any time you're doing something to become a better person, your self-esteem will go up. If your business is struggling, and you don't understand accounting, every minute you spend parked in front of the boob tube diminishes your self esteem; every minute you spend taking a class or studying a book on accounting raises your self esteem."

"And third, accept total, absolute, and uncompromising responsibility for your circumstances and your outcomes. People with low self-esteem are always making excuses and blaming other people for their problems. People with high self esteem accept that they are what they are today because of decisions they made in the past, and that they will be where they will be tomorrow because of decisions they make in the future, beginning right at the present moment."

The McDonalds lady came back and took their trash away. They each declined a second refill, so she gave them a mint.

"Let me share with you five self-esteem building action steps that I assign each of our salespeople." Charlie pulled out his steno pad and started making notes.

"The first step is to start each day by doing the thing that is most important for you to do, but which more often than not is the thing you least want to do. In many sales positions, for example, it might be making prospecting calls. Do the tough jobs first thing in the morning and the rest of the day will be a breeze."

"The second step is to program yourself with positive visions and positive self-talk. That's the purpose of those commercials I make for each of our team members."

"The third step is to pay very close attention to what you do and don't let into your mind. If you spend several hours a day watching sitcoms in which people make a mess of their lives, you increase the odds that your life will become a mess. On the other hand, if you spend your time reading books and listening to tapes that are positive and motivating, you will find yourself becoming more positive and more motivated."

"The fourth step is related, and that is to stay away from negative people and seek out positive people. Attitudes are contagious. If you hang around with negative, bitter, cynical people long enough, that's exactly what you will become yourself. If you want to be a winner, you have to associate with winners."

"And finally, number five is to be nice to other people, to have faith in them. Be a reverse paranoid, always suspecting other people of trying to help you. With an attitude like that, how can you possibly not be a success?"

It occurred to Charlie that more often that not, he assumed the worst about other people. When a customer called, he assumed it was going to be a complaint. When he called on a prospective client, he assumed he was going to be rejected. Perhaps his own expectations of other people had been the biggest stumbling block to building his business. Walking back out to the car, Charlie automatically headed for the passenger side, and had to be reminded that he was driving.

"We need to head back to the office so you can sign the forms for this loaner car," Terry said. "You also need to pick up a brochure on that new sport utility vehicle, so you can begin telling us the exact specifications you want in the one you order."

Be a reverse paranoid, Charlie reminded himself. Perhaps Terry wasn't just trying to sell another car, but really did believe that his having a Courage Place vehicle would be good for business. Charlie simply said, "Okay."

After Charlie had signed all of the forms necessary for him to use the Ferrari as his company car for the rest of the week, Terry asked him to take his steno pad out and write down one more thing, "in all caps!"

I AM THE GREATEST!!!

Charlie eased the Ferrari back out toward town and the headquarters of Milltronics, Inc. He'd been putting off calling on the CEO for some time now, and thought this might be just the day to stop by. He was beginning to feel right at home behind the wheel of the quarter-million dollar car.

Formula for believing in yourself:

1. Self-concept
2. Self-image
3. Self-esteem
4. Self-confidence

Elements of self-esteem:

1. Accept yourself as you are
2. Be willing to change
3. Accept total responsibility for your circumstances and outcome

Self-esteem building action steps

1. Start each day doing the thing that is most important for you to do
2. Program yourself with positive visions and self-talk
3. Pay close attention to what you let into your mind
4. Seek positive people, avoid negative people
5. Have faith in others

9

STAY ON TARGET

"STAYING ON TARGET."

When Charlie asked Bill Douglas the secret of his success, Douglas had answered with a question of his own: he asked Charlie if he remembered the attack scene from the end of the movie *Star Wars*. "Recall how one pilot was leading his squadron in for their bombing run, and all hell was breaking loose all around them? And he kept saying, 'Stay on target. Stay on target.' That's the secret to success in business."

"The target principle has two components — focus and concentration. Focus means having a manageable number of goals before you at any one time. The more willing you are to be focused, the more you end up being able to accomplish."

"Concentration, on the other hand, means applying all available resources to achieving that focused goal. It means staying on target, even when the world presents you with distractions that tempt you away from your target."

Bill Douglas had founded Future Perfect Now nearly twenty years ago. Now, the company was a leading provider of personal success coaching, home-study programs, as well as a library of books and tapes on success. Douglas had been one of the early pioneers in direct consumer marketing. In the early days, he didn't have money for advertising or a field sales force, so he put his successful students to work. He gave them commissions for recruiting new students. Then, as he became too busy to conduct all of the desired programs himself, he started training former students to be teachers and coaches. As the business continued to grow, many of his students started building their own regional organizations. Rather than prohibit this, Douglas created a tiered compensation program that actually encouraged this growth.

"Have you ever heard of an economist named Wilfredo Pareto?"

Charlie shook his head.

"How about the 80-20 rule?"

Charlie nodded. He was very familiar with that.

"That's the Pareto Principle," Douglas continued. "Pareto showed that almost uniformly, twenty percent of your efforts in any endeavor will yield eighty percent of your results. For a typical business, twenty percent of the customers bring in eighty percent of the revenue. In sales, twenty percent of the salespeople earn eighty percent of the commissions. In your own daily life, twenty percent of your efforts are responsible for eighty percent of your results."

"One of the secrets to success is to break out of what I call Pareto's Prison. Just imagine, if you could take the twenty percent of your efforts that yield eighty percent of your results and expand that productivity to another ten or twenty percent of your time. You would have huge leverage! Just going from twenty to thirty percent at optimal productivity doubles your results!"

The relationship between Future Perfect Now and The Courage Place had been a natural. Now in his sixth year of operation, Charlie had just opened his twentieth location, this one in Phoenix. The Courage Place had become a magnet for the type of people interested in the personal development programs offered by Future Perfect

Now, while FPN customers made the most enthusiastic members of The Courage Place.

For the past year, Charlie had tried to interest Bill Douglas in a joint venture to develop an FPN-Courage Place retreat center. Charlie saw the potential for an operation that would attract people from across the country and at the same time give him greater access to, and credibility with, the corporate community. It would also give Douglas a venue for showcasing the latest FPN programs, and for making his own headway in the corporate market, which up to now had shied away from FPN in favor of more traditional sales and management programs.

Douglas was intrigued, but each time he and Charlie spoke by phone he had expressed concern about losing focus, about "not staying on target." Cheryl Van Noyes had told Charlie that Douglas was obsessed with focus. "You might say," she told him, "that his focus is focus!" He had never entered into a joint venture with another organization. Now the two men were meeting face to face for the first time to discuss that possibility.

Douglas' office reflected the man. The walls were lined with bookshelves that seemed to be filled with every self-help book ever written. In lieu of a picture, behind Douglas' desk was an archery target with an arrow stuck in the bull's-eye.

"FPN is the world's largest publicly held private corporation." Douglas looked at Charlie and smiled at the apparent paradox. "We have thousands of shareholders around the world — 133,527 to be exact — but our stock is not traded on any market. The only way to get stock is by earning options through your performance as an FPN distributor. You should see our annual meetings. Imagine a cross between the Harvard Business School and half-time at the Super Bowl. And what has made all this possible has been," and here Douglas pointed to the target behind his desk, "a relentless focus on the target."

Charlie looked across the room at the target on the wall. He held his left arm out as if holding a bow, and with his right, pulled the imaginary string back to his ear. He said, "I'm guessing it's about twenty-five feet across your office. The chances of my hitting a bull's-eye from here are slim to none. If the target was four times bigger, however, I'd be a lot more confident." Charlie shot his fingers out straight, as though releasing the arrow, and watched its imagined arc across the room. "When you're growing your business, how do you tell the difference between an opportunity that's making the target bigger, which is a good thing, versus one that is presenting you with a brand-new target, which might not be?"

"Great question!" Douglas walked over to the target and pulled the arrow out of the bull's-eye. "I have four arrows in my quiver—attention, energy, time, and money. They are the four essential resources that every business leader must manage. If an opportunity allows me to make more productive use of those resources, meaning that the payback greatly exceeds the required incremental output, then it's probably making the target bigger. On the other hand, if the so-called new opportunity requires a great deal of attention, energy, time, or money relative to the payback, then it's creating a new target that takes my eye off the one bull's-eye which is essential to the success of my business."

Douglas laid the arrow on his desk. "Cheryl mentioned that you're friends with Mitch Matsui, the guy who translates all those McZen poems." Charlie nodded, "Yeah. In fact, the seeds of my own business were planted when Mitch and I spent a week in the Grand Canyon several years ago."

Douglas stuck his hands in his pockets and looked out the window. "I must have flown over the Grand Canyon a thousand times, but I've never been down in it. I've heard it described as God's most magnificent natural cathedral. Let me know if you guys go again. I'd love to tag along, if you don't mind."

"As a matter of fact, we're planning a trip for early October. I'll send you some information."

"Thanks. That'd be great. And I'd also love to meet Mitch. I really get a kick out of those McZen poems he writes."

"Mitch swears he doesn't write them, that there really is a poet named McZen, and that all Mitch does is translate his poems from the original Chinese calligraphy. He's even shown me a few of the originals, which are absolutely elegant."

"Well, I'd still love to meet him—and Master McZen, if that's possible." Charlie hadn't noticed before, but on the coffee table was one of Mitch's latest McZen translations: *The Sound of One Hand Working*, which included some of McZen's more irreverent thoughts on work life in America. "There's so much truth in these poems, and especially this one," Douglas said as he held the open book to Charlie, who read this poem:

> *Attention.*
> *May I have your attention please?*
> *It's a gift so often requested.*
> *So grundgingly given.*
> *So rarely appreciated.*

"It's like he says," Douglas continued, "your attention is your most precious resource, which is why people say *pay* attention. More than anything else, attention is a limited resource, because you can only pay attention to one thing at a time. People are successful to the extent that they make a conscious choice what they want to pay attention to. Some of the most miserable people in the world are those who choose to pay attention to bad news, and never see the good news."

As Douglas was talking, Charlie had been alternately looking out the window and scanning the books on the shelves. Suddenly, he burst out laughing. "What's so funny," Douglas asked.

"Another one of McZen's little poems talks about how there are many roads to success, and it's a darn good thing, too. You've built this magnificent business empire by keeping your focus on a tiny little bull's-eye. That's something I could never do."

"Of course you could," Douglas replied. "It just takes discipline, and the will to succeed."

"You know, Bill, for a long time I believed that. Because I was so easily distracted, I figured I must have some sort of a character defect. And finally, I read a book about adult attention deficit disorder. I'll tell you, it was like looking in a mirror. The book described me so exactly, that I actually went to see a psychiatrist for a diagnosis."

"When I went in for my results, the doctor told me he had good news and bad news. The good news, he said, was that I did not have ADD. The bad news was that I had RBADD — *really bad* attention deficit disorder."

Both men laughed, then Charlie continued: "I read a book that said that people with ADD actually make great entrepreneurs, because we're always scanning the horizon for opportunities and pursuing them when they arise. We make great hunters. Unfortunately, we don't make very good farmers, because our idea of long-term planning is wondering what's for dinner, not planting something in May and waiting for a harvest in October."

Douglas laughed. "I guess I'd never looked at it that way. I would consider myself more of a farmer, and each of the people in my organization are the plants I'm cultivating."

"Well, one of the things this book said," Charlie continued, "was that when a farmer and a hunter team up together, they can make an unbeatable combination. Maybe that would be one way we could work well together — I could bring a lot of energy, and you could help focus it."

"Maybe so," Douglas said, nodding thoughtfully. "Maybe so. As I said, energy is the second arrow in my quiver. Most people spend their energy the way a dandelion spreads its seeds, thoughtlessly tossing it out to whatever happens to be in front of them and hoping something good will happen. When the big opportunity comes, they don't have the energy to pursue it because they've wasted it."

"I've got my own theory about energy," Charlie said. "I think it's a logrhythmic function."

"What do you mean by that?" Douglas asked.

"Energy expenditure has a geometric impact. One unit of energy at the end of a project is worth a lot more than the same unit of energy at the beginning of a project. Think about it. When you're getting something new started, everybody has a ton of energy because they're all excited and enthusiastic. But after weeks of long days and late nights energy becomes a much more rare commodity. It's at the point where you most want to quit that another pint or so of gas in the tank could push you past the checkered flag. I always ask people to imagine running a hundred yard dash. The closer you get to the victory tape, the more your legs hurt and your lungs burn."

"That's a great metaphor." Douglas said. "I'll have to remember that. The third arrow in my quiver is time."

"The universal and unsolvable metaphysical mystery," Charlie said. "I once read that time is simply God's way of keeping everything from happening all at once."

"Yeah," Douglas laughed, "well, if more people would turn off the TV, get their butts out of the easy chair, and get busy, then there would be a lot less anxiety and a lot more wealth in this world. So many people never achieve their goals because they kill time, and killing time is nothing less than killing life itself. Procrastination is stealing time from tomorrow so you can avoid what you should be doing today, which leaves you permanently living in the shadow of yesterday. Time is money, they say, but only if you use it effectively. And money is the fourth essential resource."

"It's funny, everybody thinks that money is so important in business, but in my book it's the least essential of the four resources. One of my early mentors in business gave me some advice I've always tried to follow. In business school, we learned that ROI — return on investment — is one of the most important indicators of long-term wealth. Most business people pay lots of attention to the 'R' — increasing sales to grow their revenue, forgetting the fact that you can just as effectively increase ROI by minimizing the 'I.' Even today, with all our success, we are extremely careful about how we spend our money."

"More than two thousand years ago, Lao Tzu said that the sage is ruthless. I think if he were in the room today, he would agree that to be successful you have to be ruthless first of all with yourself. You must ruthlessly eradicate negative attitudes and cultivate positive ones."

Douglas nodded, and picked up where Charlie had left off. "You have to ruthlessly guard your energy, and channel it into only the most productive activities. And you have to be ruthlessly productive with your time. Every minute, every hour, you must be asking yourself if what you are about to do is the most important action you can take to move you in the direction of achieving your goals."

"And you have to be ruthless in how you spend your money," Douglas concluded. "There are a million temptations out there, and it's easy to come up with reasons why you need every one of them. The road to wealth is built through ruthless control of desires."

Douglas looked silently out the window. At length, he said, "You mentioned Lao Tzu a few minutes ago. At about the same time he was writing his poetry, the Persian army of King Darius had landed an invasion force on the shores of Greece, at a place called Marathon. The Greek army was badly outnumbered. Many of the Greek generals wanted to retreat back toward Athens, but Miltiades prevailed upon a council of war to attack first thing in the morning. The Greeks did not just march across the field towards the Persians, they hit them at a dead run. Speed — and concentration — made up for a deficit of arms. The Greeks swept the Persians from the field, in what might have been one of the most important battles of all time. But for Marathon, our world might not have been shaped by the thinking of Socrates, Plato, and Aristotle."

"So, let's marshal our forces and move quickly." Feeling the emotion he had once interpreted as terror, but which Nick Amatuzzo taught him to recognize as exhilaration welling up inside, Charlie knew he'd found a vital partner for helping him reach his memory of the future.

"Winston Churchill once said that there is only one thing worse than fighting with allies, and that's fighting without them," Douglas replied. Shaking Charlie's hand, he said, "Let's make the target bigger, and then let's stay on target!"

RESOURCES BUSINESS LEADERS MUST MANAGE:

1.   Attention
2.   Energy
3.   Time
4.   Money

10

KEEP MOVING

CHUCK HARTIKOFF BILLED HIMSELF AS "THE COACH FOR BUSINESS Athletes." He had become one of the favorite instructors at The Courage Place, and now was on a regular schedule that took him to each center at least twice a year. He was the keynote speaker for the dedication of The Courage Place Convention Center, the joint venture Charlie McKeever and Bill Douglas had agreed upon almost two years earlier.

Chuck was the personal success coach for more than 250 Courage Place members around the country, and the feedback Charlie had received was tremendous. Charlie had sent each of them a questionnaire asking, among other things, to estimate by how much their income had increased as a result of Chuck's coaching. The answer had astounded him—-the total was over $5,000,000 in the previous year. In fact, Charlie had been so impressed with the comments that he'd personally signed up to participate with Chuck's system, and had not been disappointed. Now, Chuck was in his element, up on the platform, holding court for more than 2,000 entrepreneurs and executives, eager to learn his secrets of success for business athletes.

"The first thing you have to do," he shouted, "is overcome the Terrible Toos and the Big Buts! You've all heard them, haven't you?"

> *I'd love to start my own business, but I'm too deep in debt.*
>
> *I'd make more sales calls today, but I'm too far behind on my paperwork.*
>
> *I'd go out for a run today, but I'm just too tired after all the hassles at work.*

The audience roared. Charlie smiled as he looked across the crowd, knowing that the people laughing loudest were most likely to be seeing their own excuses ridiculed up on the stage. Hartikoff continued:

> *I'd love to think and grow rich, but I'm too busy to think.*
>
> *I'd love to have more fun, but my wife is such a wet blanket!*
>
> *I'd love to travel more, but my deadbeat husband won't earn enough money.*
>
> *I'd love to live my dreams, but, but, but,... I'm too, too, too...*

People were laughing so hard that many were doubled over with tears running down their cheeks. By the time he was done, Hartikoff had zinged just about everybody. "Until you conquer the Terrible Toos and the Big Buts, your dreams and wishes will remain just that — dreams and wishes. You must change 'I would, *but I'm too...*' to 'I will, *and I'll start by...*'"

Hartikoff was moving across the stage. "You've got to move physically! You've got to move emotionally! You've got to move spiritually! You've got to be like a shark! You know what happens to a shark if it stops swimming, don't you? It sinks and dies! And you will too, if you don't keep moving."

Hartikoff was really starting to roll now. "One of the most exciting developments in all of science today is the field of psychoneuroimmunology. That is PSYCHO—your thinking mind; NEURO—your physical brain; IMMUNOLOGY—your body's health. What researchers have learned is that there is an inextricable interconnection between your body, your mind, and your spirit. This body-mind-spirit nexus is as essential to your success in business as it is to your success in life. You have to exercise all three — body, mind, and spirit — every single day."

Hartikoff pulled a jump rope from out of a box and began skipping right up there on the stage. "Being successful in business is hard work, isn't it?" As he continued jumping, he said, "Leadership requires stamina — real physical stamina, doesn't it?" There was a resounding chorus of "YES!"

"But everyone else is exercising, so if you really want to be a winner, you must do more than what everyone else is doing, right?" As the audience responded, Hartikoff kicked his jump rope into high speed, and started high stepping through each rotation. "My competition does it fast, so I do it faster! They do it with two legs," and he increased the speed of the rope further still, and hopped through it on one leg. The audience roared their approval.

"How many of you saw the article in the paper this morning about the local company that had a layoff in the wake of a merger?" Many hands went up. "It's happening all over, isn't it? Welcome to the future! Companies will continue re-organizing, and jobs will continue to be eliminated."

"So let's say we talked to two people after the lay-off today. The first person is scared to death — has visions of bankruptcy and homelessness. The second person reads the same newspaper we all read this morning, but instead of focusing on the article about the layoff, his attention is grabbed by the article saying that more jobs have been created by entrepreneurial businesses this year than in any previous year. He's especially taken by the comment that almost nobody gets rich working for someone else, and that in the previous year more entrepreneurs became millionaires than any other year in our nation's history."

"Now, imagine it's two years from now. Where are those two men likely to be?" Hartikoff paused for a moment. "I'll tell you where they are. Person number one did not become bankrupt and homeless. As you might expect, he eventually found another job doing very much the same thing he was doing before. And he wakes up every day with the fear that it could happen again. Every time he's called into the boss' office he trembles at the prospect of another pink slip. And of course, it's just a matter of time before his fear becomes a self-fulfilling prophecy, isn't it?"

"Now the second man had the same reasons to be afraid, but had the courage to stand up to his fears with determination. He resolved to himself that it would never happen again, that never again would he place control of his destiny in someone else's hands. He decided to start his own business. In the short run, he may or may not make more money than person number one, but at least he has set the stage for creating the kind of wealth that person number one can only imagine."

"Physical exercise," Hartikoff continued, "is a spur to mental creativity. In a recent study, researchers gave a problem to two different groups of people and asked them to solve it. Those in the first group were placed in comfortable easy chairs to work on their problem. People from the second group were asked to ride an exercise bike while they cogitated. Guess who came up with better solutions? With more creative and more workable solutions? That's right! The people in the second group, on their exercise bikes. Think about it; how many times have you gone out for a walk or a run or a bike ride, and experienced one of those brilliant, creative flashes?"

"Now, in addition to your physical health, you also have to take care of your emotional health. And the first step is to lighten up and have more fun. Far too many of us are 'dead serious,' but I'll tell you this; if you're *dead serious* for long enough, you'll end up *seriously dead*. It happens emotionally before it happens physically. We all know people who are as dead as doornails, they just haven't stopped breathing yet so we can bury them without breaking the law!"

"The second thing you can do to promote your emotional health," Hartikoff went on, "is to practice living in the present here and now. Ladies and gentlemen, virtually all emotional pain is caused by time travel. It's either regret, guilt, and anger from the past, anxiety or fear and worry about the future. Almost by definition, if you can keep your attention focused on what's right in front of you at each moment, you'll find the world such a beautiful place that there is no room for emotional pain. You'll also find yourself a lot more productive."

"Have you ever noticed, no matter what it is you're doing, in the back of your mind you're always thinking that there's something else more important that you should be doing? It's like the guy that's working at the office, and feeling guilty that he's not at home with the family. So what does he do? He packs all of his paperwork into a briefcase and hauls it home, to be with the family. Then all evening he feels guilty that he's not working on what's in the briefcase."

There were laughs of recognition, including from Charlie, who had caught himself thinking that he should be with his accountants working on the upcoming direct public offering rather than listening to Hartikoff.

"The third step to emotional health," Hartikoff continued, "is to see the world as it really is. And for most of us, that requires learning how to forget. The world is changing so fast that what you knew yesterday may not be true anymore today. The single most powerful obstacle to your future success will be the inaccurate picture you have of yourself today. Forget what you think you can't do! Forget what you think you don't know! Forget what people have told you about your limitations! Forget all the Terrible Toos and the Big Buts that are holding you back!"

"The fourth thing I'm going to tell you about emotional health may sound like it contradicts the whole theme of this program, but it doesn't."

"Your emotional health demands that you have times of rest, relaxation, and recuperation. And here are two suggestions for doing that. First, re-introduce into your life the ancient concept of a Sabbath — a day of rest. By that, I do not mean sitting like a boiled vegetable in front of the boob tube," — laughs of embarrassed recognition from the audience — "but rather, giving yourself one day every week for reading, thinking, writing in your journal, dreaming."

"The other thing I recommend is periodic Neuro-Attitudinal Positioning. Has everybody heard of Neuro-Attitudinal Positioning, or what's most commonly known as N.A.P.? I mean, of course, taking a nap. When you're fatigued, you are more likely to feel confused and anxious. Sometimes, a bit of N.A.P. can be just what the doctor ordered to restore your energy, courage, and faith."

"And speaking of faith, the final thing I want to talk about today is spiritual health. I'll give you two practical and specific suggestions. The first is to follow the advice of Jesus, and pray continuously. Pray for guidance, strength, courage, compassion, wisdom, and all the other virtues you must have to become the person you want to be — the person you are destined to be. Be like Tevye in the movie *Fiddler on the Roof* — always talking to God."

"Second, learn how to listen for the answers. The world has gotten so loud and busy, that we don't often take time to listen for the still, soft voice of God, speaking in response to our prayers."

"There are many forms of meditation. In Zen, you sit quietly, slowly allowing the mind to empty. In transcendental meditation, you use a mantra to crowd out all the inner voices. In centering prayer, you repeat a short scriptural passage to bring about a sense of inner stillness. It matters much less how you achieve this stillness — than that you take the time to do it. It is from that inner stillness that your outer power will arise."

Hartikoff was about to break the audience into small groups to work on their individual action plans. Charlie looked at his watch and smiled. He still had plenty of time to speak with the accountants. Hartikoff was right, he thought. You can get a lot more done if you limit yourself to doing one thing at a time, keeping your attention in the present. He took one last look at Hartikoff, now answering questions for a line of people standing before the stage, then headed out into the parking lot where his red Ferrari was proudly parked in the front row.

Promote emotional health:
1. Lighten up
2. Live in the present
3. Learn to see the world as it really is
4. Balance action and recuperation

Promote spiritual health:
1. Pray
2. Learn to listen for the answers

11

SERVE YOUR WAY TO GREATNESS

ONCE A MONTH, CHARLIE MET WITH THE ENTIRE MANAGEMENT TEAM OF The Courage Place through the magic of video-conferencing. He could almost maintain the same feel of personal closeness that had developed in the early days, even though now there were more than 300 locations across the United States and Canada, with the first European center scheduled to open the following year. Several years earlier, the company had gone public by selling shares of stock to its members in a direct public offering. Now, the monthly management meeting was also open to member-owners by means of a special Internet hook-up.

For the most part, going public had been a tremendous step forward for the company. The sale of stock had provided capital that was essential for maintaining an aggressive schedule of opening new centers, as well as developing new product and service lines. More important in Charlie's eyes, when members "graduated" to become part-owners of The Courage Place, their commitment and enthusiasm increased geometrically. The downside of going public was a natural tendency for many Courage Place managers to focus more on quarterly earnings and the stock price than on the core service business. Today, Charlie wanted to discuss not just the business of service, but also the philosophy of serving.

As he always did, Charlie began by addressing some of the common concerns that had been raised by managers during the previous month, and by answering questions that had been sent to him by owner-members via e-mail. Charlie used this period to get people to relax, lighten up, and think about things from a new perspective. From his years of public speaking, he had learned that before you can teach somebody something, you must touch them emotionally.

"Because we are in the business of helping people create better lives for themselves, The Courage Place has always attracted people who have an incredible service orientation. Now, that's a good thing — those are exactly the kind of people we want to attract. But in the early days, when we were just getting this business started, I had to continuously remind people that even though we had a powerful service mission, we still were a business, and as a business, we had to make a profit. We must make a healthy profit so that we have the funds to reinvest into new and improved programs to serve our clients more effectively, and to keep reaching out to bring new members into the fold."

"But if we lose sight of the mission that brought us all into this business in the first place, if we begin to let the quality of our service slip, we open the door for someone else to come in and take our business away from us."

At first, Charlie had found it difficult to speak to a camera with the same passion and enthusiasm that a live audience brought forth. Now, he was able to quickly get into the flow by imagining the faces on the other side of the camera.

"My friend Mitch Matsui introduced me to the poetry of McZen. It's quirky and full of paradox, but contains great wisdom about life. One of my favorites reads:

Someone with a job is never secure.
Someone with a calling is never unemployed.

"That's so true. In today's turbulent world, nobody can go to work for a company and be confident that just by being loyal, reliable, and competent, they'll still be there in twenty or thirty years. Even the CEO is accountable to a board, and boards everywhere — including the board at The Courage Place — are becoming more demanding, and willing to replace a CEO who doesn't perform."

"While job security may be an illusion, finding the security of a calling is rock solid. If you see your work as a calling, and not simply the means to a paycheck, there will never be a day in your life that you can't find meaningful work to do. Of course, there may be days when the pay is low — but there is always work to be done."

"We must all strive to see our work as a calling, and to put love into that work. If we do that, I'm convinced that the bottom line will grow naturally and we will all prosper. With the new responsibilities we have to our member-owners, we naturally feel more pressure to maintain profits and keep the stock price going up. Trust me," Charlie laughed, "I feel this more than anyone. I have one board member who goes on line the minute the stock market opens each morning, and then phones me up to tell me what our stock price is at that moment."

"We must manage our business effectively, but must never fall victim to the siren song of the market. There are many companies that march to the drum of their own long-term vision rather than dance to the piper of Wall Street. Companies like ServiceMaster, Hewlett Packard, Johnson & Johnson, and many others have made the commitment to put their people first — to serve their employees, customers, and communities — and trust that profits and higher stock prices would follow."

"It's the great paradox of service. About twenty-five hundred years ago, Confucius said that if you want to be successful, the best way is to help other people be successful. It was true then, and it's true today. Another Chinese philosopher, Chuang Tzu, said the only way to find happiness is to not do anything calculated to achieve your own happiness. In other words, to lose yourself in the joy of work for its own sake, and to helping others be happy."

Charlie took a call from one of the newer managers. "We've been asked by one of the local schools, which happens to be in a lower income community, to put together a program that will help them teach their students some of the emotional skills that are required to succeed in the workplace, and as entrepreneurs. I really want to do it, but I'm having a hard time justifying the resources that would be required, especially since for some strange reason, my employees are pretty insistent about being paid on a consistent basis. How do you suggest I evaluate a situation like this?"

"That's a very important question. First of all, let me say that there is not a one-size-fits-all answer, and that you have to evaluate your own individual circumstances. Having said that, let me point out that opportunities for gain frequently come disguised as calls to service. What you need is some creative thinking. Is there a local corporation that would be willing to sponsor the program? Can you donate the program to the school, but in return have them sponsor a companion program for parents with a modest registration fee to help you offset your costs? In return for you doing the program, will the school offer membership in The Courage Place as an optional benefit to its faculty and staff? With a bit of imagination, you can often find a win-win solution that allows you to be profitable."

The next caller was Jan Marcheson, who operated a very successful Courage Place center in San Francisco. She often asked the tough questions that were on everyone's mind. "You know, Charlie, I buy in to everything you're saying a thousand percent. But some days, I feel like a hypocrite because I'm out there in the classroom telling people to face their fears with courage, and then I go back to my office and

150

close the door and just darn near collapse under the weight of my own fears. How do you walk the talk when you don't even feel like you can get out of the wheelchair?"

"Let me say two things about that, Jan. First, you *are* walking the talk. There's not a person involved with The Courage Place who hasn't at one time or another felt overwhelmed by their fears and problems. Does anyone out there disagree?" There was no response, so Charlie continued.

"It takes incredible strength and courage to close the door to your office behind you, to lock your fears and your problems inside, and to go stand in front of an audience and give them the inspiration to pursue their dreams. How could you possibly empathize with their problems if you didn't occasionally walk in their shoes, or sit in their wheelchairs?"

"The second thing we must recognize is that many of us came to The Courage Place because courage is what we ourselves most needed. By teaching it, we gain it. Many years ago, Dr. Jared Mitchell shared with me a learning philosophy he'd picked up in his surgical residency, which still keeps me motivated to teach before I may feel ready:

See one, do one, teach one

We must never forget to apply in our own lives what we teach others — that caring is the antidote to anxiety, and service is the treatment for adversity."

"You've all heard my lecture on the fear of success, which is far more toxic than the fear of failure. One of the most powerful weapons I know of to overcome the fear of success is a commitment to serve other people. Once you adopt this, you know that the more successful you become, the more service you can provide to other people."

" I'd like to close with two final points. First, service always springs from an attitude of gratitude — thankfulness for what we've been blessed with in the past, for what we have right now, and for the future blessings we anticipate. There's nothing you can't be thankful for, even your weaknesses and the adversities that cross your path, as these often help guide you toward the destiny that is authentically yours."

"Finally, when it comes to service, striving is more important than achieving. Someone once asked Mother Theresa why she wasted her time helping the poor, since there were so many of them, and she could never be successful at eliminating their problems. In response, she snapped that she was not there to be successful; she was there to be faithful. Ultimately, our service is a reflection of our faith. It's a big part of what The Courage Place is all about."

As he usually did, Charlie ended the meeting by outlining some of the company's key plans and priorities for the coming months. Driving from the studio back to his office, something Alan Silvermane had said several years ago popped back into his head; "Dream Beyond the Dream." Charlie knew that the time would soon come when he'd turn over the reigns of The Courage Place to someone else, and he would need to start thinking about what service he would provide during the next phase of his own life.

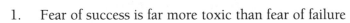

1. Fear of success is far more toxic than fear of failure
2. Service springs from an attitude of gratitude
3. Striving is more important than achieving

12

EXPECT A MIRACLE

CHARLIE SAT LOOKING AT THE WALLS OF HIS OFFICE, WHICH WERE NOW almost completely bare since his personal photos and paintings had been removed. This would be the last time he would sit behind his desk as chief executive officer of The Courage Place. The night before, there had been a wonderful retirement party. In several hours, Brian Hunter would move into the job for which he had been preparing for the past several years.

Charlie had long thought about what final words of wisdom he would pass on to his successor. On the desk were four things that had been very special to him, which he would now give to Brian. The first was a simple needlepoint that Pam had made shortly after they decided to leave the corporate world and start The Courage Place. It said only:

Mark 9:23

It was Charlie's favorite passage from *The Bible*. "All things are possible for one who believes." He had told the story a thousand times. How upon coming down from the mountain Jesus was walking through a crowd when a man broke through and implored Him to heal his son. "Can you help?" the man pleaded. But Jesus turned the question right back around: "Can *you* help? All things are possible to one who believes." And how even two millennia after the fact, one could still feel the anguish—and the hope—in the man's voice as he replied, "I believe. Help me overcome my unbelief."

In all of His miracles, Charlie would say, Jesus never took personal credit. More often than not, He attributed the miracle to the one being healed: "Your faith has made you well; your faith has made you whole." Partial faith is faith enough to begin, and once you begin, faith will grow.

As Charlie waited for Brian to join him, he thought about how many times in the past thirty years he had wanted so much to believe in his dreams, his memories of the future, yet struggled to silence his inner Gollum. How many times the only thing standing between him and failure had been his faith, and how often that faith was tenuous. And yet, even that tiny seed of faith had, in the long run, been faith enough.

Those first dreams that he and Pam had shared together seemed so big, so impossible, at the time. "Not in ten lifetimes," Gollum had laughed, "could you fulfill even one tenth of that vision. Memories of the future? Hah! More like delusions of grandeur." Fortunately, Charlie had eventually learned how to tame Gollum. In retrospect, those dreams that once seemed so immense were actually pretty puny.

The second thing Charlie planned to give Brian was a small laminated card he had carried in his wallet from the very beginning. It was now quite tattered from having been read more than ten thousand times—every morning and every evening for three decades. It was a quote by Napoleon Hill:

> *Every successful person finds that great success lies just beyond the point where they're convinced their idea is not going to work.*

Over the years, Charlie had made many mistakes and experienced many apparent failures. In the years to come, Brian Hunter would do likewise. Charlie hoped that this small inspiration would be as helpful to Brian as it had been to him.

The third item that Charlie was going to leave was the paperweight which had sat on top of his desk from the very beginning. It was a piece of granite into which were carved the most powerful three words in the world:

Expect A Miracle

Over the years, Charlie had come not just to hope for miracles and to pray for them, but to expect them. That attitude was as much a part of his business strategy as doing market research.

Charlie walked over to the window and looked out across the campus. Everything he saw had once been an impossible dream. "It'll take a miracle," one of his board members had commented when he shared the vision of a headquarters campus that would include a conference center, retreat center, complete gymnasium facilities, and the world's most comprehensive motivational resource center. Charlie smiled as he watched a crowd making its way from the parking lot to the convention center. Louisa Sheldon Henderson was speaking today.

When she had come to Charlie's very first Courage Place event thirty years ago, she was a young single mother struggling with depression, bulimia, and even serious thoughts of suicide. Fewer than ten people had showed up for that program, and Charlie had felt more like crying than speaking. How could he have known that he was planting the seeds for miracles in other people's lives that far-off winter morning at the Downtown Gym? Today, one of those miracles was coming full circle as Louisa, who had since become one of the country's most popular speakers, brought her message of hope and courage to The Courage Place Convention Center. She was now planting the seeds for future miracles.

People so often misunderstand what a miracle is—and what is not, Charlie thought. A miracle is not a magic trick. It's less a matter of turning water into wine, and more a matter of turning a wino into a water drinker. A miracle is not instant relief from the problems of life. More often than not, the chief ingredient in making miracles is the simple passage of time. Jesus had said that when you pray, if you pray as though your prayer had already been answered, it will be. So often people are tempted to lose faith when their prayers aren't answered *right now.*

Nor is a miracle a guarantee of success or security. Charlie often heard people complain about lack of security, and he would remind them that the Lord's Prayer said nothing at all about tomorrow's bread, it asks only that we be given our bread today. Sometimes the greatest miracle was to be grateful for today's bread—the blessings of the present—and to have faith that tomorrow's bread would arrive on time.

Many of us, Charlie reflected, don't believe in miracles because they frighten us. If miracles are possible, even foreseeable, that could mean we should hold ourselves to a higher standard of expectation. Charlie smiled as he thought of Saint Peter walking on the water. At first it was wonderful, this being able to walk upon the surface of a lake, just as Jesus had told him he could if he believed he could. But once out there on the water, his nerve deserted him and he began to sink.

What a perfect metaphor for the fear of success, the fear of commitment, that prevents so many people from achieving their full potential. We climb out of the boat of familiarity and security and start to walk out there on the water of exploration and adventure. Then, when we find ourselves achieving the miracle that for so long had merely been an impossible dream, we start to sink. The weight of fear and doubt pushes us down and we holler, "Save me!" as we frantically make our way back to the boat. Ironically, in a turbulent world the only real security lies in leaving the perceived safety of the boat.

Expect a miracle, but don't give God a deadline. Most of the miracle-making process is invisible. It's going on below the surface. The ultimate miracle is not something that happens "out there", but rather is a profound transformation that happens inside, in the head and in the heart.

The fourth thing Charlie was going to leave Brian was an eagle's feather encased in Lucite. One day, Charlie had been sitting up on a bluff overlooking a river. It was perhaps at the darkest moment of his life. After several years of struggling, there was the very real possibility that The Courage Place would go under. He had not even come close to meeting his financial projections, was deep in debt, and dodging phone calls from creditors. He contemplated the possibility of bankruptcy, but knew in his heart that not even that drastic step would give him the fresh start he seemed to need at that moment. In a moment of intense self pity, he even found himself wishing God would take his life, because he didn't have the courage to do it himself.

After an hour or so of watching the river flow by, his cares receded somewhat and he began to enjoy the warm sun and the soft breeze. Then he experienced a feeling he'd never had before; it was at once the tranquility of inner peace and the exhilaration of great anticipation. At that moment, there was an eagle coursing along the river in his direction. When it reached the bend, the great bird continued straight, right in Charlie's direction. As it flew over, the bird tilted slightly and seemed to look down right at Charlie. It circled back around, lower this time. On the next pass, the bird actually landed right there on the bluff, not ten feet away.

Charlie sat still as stone, not wanting to disturb the magic. He loved eagles and all other birds of prey, and had let himself believe that whenever he saw one, it was simply God sending a message of reassurance. The bird just stood there, pacing up and down like a soldier marching in place, and then stretched his wings and squawked loudly, as if warning the world that this was his territory and he would protect it with his life. Charlie had the feeling that he, too, would fall under the great bird's protection. Then the eagle folded his wings and settled in with his chest puffed out and his head held high, like some ancient warrior at his duty post. The breeze flowed through his feathers, and it almost seemed as if he was smiling, proud and magnificent..

Charlie looked more closely at the bird, and could see that his authority had been hard-won. Seen up close, his feathers were tattered, and he had a deep scar running the length of one leg. As the bird cocked his head in Charlie's direction, he could see that it had lost an eye.

Standing behind his desk, Charlie felt a sudden warmth of affection for that bird he had seen only once, so long ago. He could see it as clearly as though it had happened that very morning. The bird had watched Charlie for a long time through its one eye, then bobbed its head up and down as though he were saying, "Yes" to him. The last thing he remembered before falling asleep was hearing his guardian eagle squawking loudly and flapping his wings, as though broadcasting a warning to the world that Charlie was not to be disturbed.

Charlie never did know for sure whether that eagle came to him in the world of physical reality or in the world of dreams. He was never certain that the tattered feather he found in the grass had come from this guardian eagle, or by some coincidence had been sitting there all along. It really didn't matter. From that moment forward, Charlie knew with absolute certainty that he would not be allowed to fail in his mission. He might have struggles, might have his feathers battered or even lose an eye, but as long as he did not quit, he would prevail. In the years since, whenever it seemed that he was losing the battle, Charlie recalled that eagle who, if anything, was made even more majestic by his scars, and resolved to fight on.

My scars may not be as visible as the eagle's were, Charlie thought, but they are every bit as real. And now, my role in life will be to serve for Brian and the others in the way that eagle has served me—as a distant guardian. Charlie looked again at the four items on the desk. Then he laughed. Of all people, Brian Hunter did not need a motivational speech when he occupied this office. The two men would simply make small talk, and reminisce for a while. Then Charlie would leave. On his way out the door he would repeat the words that had guided him for so long:

Dream a big dream,
make it a memory of the future, and expect a miracle.

1. "All things are possible to one who believes."
2. "Every successful person finds that great success lies just beyond the point where they're convinced their idea is not going to work."
3. "Expect a miracle—but don't give God a deadline."
4. Dream a big dream, make it a memory of the future, and expect a miracle.

Epilogue:

Dream Beyond the Dream

THE MORNING CHILL HAD LONG SINCE EVAPORATED, SO CHARLIE HAD TIED his flannel hiking shirt to the outside of his backpack to let it dry. Almost exactly thirty years ago, he had written down in his *Dreamcyclopedia* his goal to spend a week alone hiking in the Grand Canyon. He'd never thought it would take this long, but now here he was, high on a ledge overlooking the Colorado River. He had not seen another human being in four days.

It was hard to maintain the appropriate state of awe in this magnificent cathedral, where every vista seemed to outdo the one before. As he rounded a corner, Charlie saw a hollow in the limestone wall that just seemed to cry out for him to stop and take a break. Dropping his backpack onto the ground, he extracted a bag of gorp, his water bottle, and his journal. He picked up his walking stick and turned it slowly in his hands, again reading each of the names that had been meticulously carved into it.

Each name brought back a memory, a memory of somebody who had helped him build The Courage Place into a worldwide phenomenon—- more a movement than a business — through which thousands of people had found a sense of direction, and the courage and determination to follow it. The business had grown in many directions that Charlie would never have anticipated in the early days, and the dream continued to get bigger and bigger.

The walking stick had been a gift at his retirement party several months earlier. It was presented to him by Cheryl Van Noyes, who had become Chairman of Future Perfect Now upon the retirement of Bill Douglas. "Just as we have leaned on you throughout the years," she said in her remarks, "now we want you to know that you can lean on us wherever your trail leads you." Charlie knew that was why he was in the Grand Canyon at this time, and why the trip had been delayed for so long. Thirty years ago, Alan Silvermane had told him to "Dream Beyond the Dream." Charlie hoped that Silvermane would have been proud of what he'd accomplished. The thirty-six year old Charlie who'd sat in the office with Silvermane would certainly have been astounded to review the accomplishments of the sixty-five year old man he would someday become.

Although not many people knew the name Charlie McKeever, The Courage Place had become one of the world's most familiar institutions. There was a Courage Place in every hospital, every airport, every shopping center, everywhere in the world. Every day, millions of people across the globe logged onto The Courage Place web site for a daily dose of education and inspiration. Courage Place graduates had started businesses which created millions of new jobs; served in local, state, and federal government at all levels; had started non-profit organizations and social service agencies to deal with the world's most pressing problems. And to Charlie, most important of all, had become teachers, instructing the next generation on courage and perseverance.

Now the time had come for Charlie to dream beyond the dream. He had plenty of money and, he hoped, a lot more time to continue making a difference. For some time, he had been writing down ideas in his journal. He'd whittled that list down to a few that really excited him. In the next few days, he would decide upon one of them. Charlie opened the journal and reviewed his list again. It would be a tough choice. Looking down the river, he saw a tiny spot slowly growing larger as it came closer. It was unusual, he thought, to see a crow so high, flying solo, kiting the wind along the river. As it came closer, it squawked loudly, and Charlie realized that this was not a crow.

It was an eagle. It coasted down the river, like an angel dancing on the breath of God, closer to Charlie. When it was not twenty yards away, the eagle tilted on one wing and flew so close that Charlie could almost have reached out and touched it with his walking stick. Now right above Charlie, the eagle swooped down and squawked once more. Charlie looked up into the face of his guardian eagle. He had only one eye.

Charlie closed his eyes and closed his journal, and smiled into the sun. He would sleep for awhile. And dream. A new dream. A big dream. The dream beyond the dream.